Science Web Pupil Book 1

Peter Horsfall and Pat O'Brien

Introduction

A message for the reader

This Science Web Pupil Book includes a number of features that will support you in learning about science at Key Stage 3.

Each **Unit** starts off with a two page spread which introduces the key learning ideas it covers.

Starting Points outlines what you should know about before studying this Unit.

Learning Objectives explain what you will learn by studying the Unit, and trying out the questions.

Key Words that you will meet in the Unit are listed in alphabetical order.

A **Learning Summary** presents all of the main ideas in the Unit on one page. Several different methods of doing this are shown in different Units.

You are encouraged to try out these methods in making your own summary of learning, after studying a Unit.

Within each Unit, learning is supported by **challenging questions** alongside the text. These are intended to promote thinking and reflection on the ideas being studied.

End of Unit questions provide an opportunity to check understanding after study. These questions model Key Stage 3 End of Unit test questions and may be used for revision.

Answers to the End of Unit questions are provided on the web site at:

www.scienceweb.co.uk

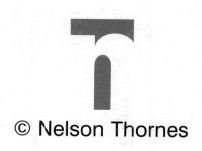

Published in 2001 by:
Nelson Thornes Ltd
Delta Place
27 Bath Road
CHELTENHAM
GL53 7TH
United Kingdom

01 02 03 04 05 / 10 9 8 7 6 5 4 3 2 1

A catalogue record for this book is available from the British Library

ISBN 0 17 438746 6

Illustrations by Tim Oliver
Page make-up by Cambridge Publishing Management

Printed and bound in Spain by Graficas Estella

Acknowledgements

The authors and publisher would like to thank the following people who supplied photographs.

Cover Photos: Space Shuttle, Globe, Space/Neptune, Pylon (Digital Vision), Cells (Digital Stock).

Andrew Lambert: 55 (top), 70, 71 (top), 71 (bottom), 72, 73 (top), 73 (bottom), 78 (bottom), 80 (top), 77 (bottom left), 79 (top), 93 (bottom), 95, 97, 100, 107 (bottom), 110 (top left), 110 (top right), 110 (bottom left), 110 (bottom right), 125 (top left), 130, 134, 138, 141, 142. *Archivi Alinari:* 64 (bottom left). *A–Z Botanical Collection Ltd:* 17 (bottom right – John Banurji). *B & C Alexander:* 124 (top). *Biophoto Associates:* 15 (bottom), 38 (bottom). *Britstock-IFA:* 113 (TPL). *Bubbles Photo Library:* 44 (middle – Angela Hampton), 46 (bottom – Ian West), 69 (Frans Rombout), 135 (top left – Jennie Woodcock). *Collections:* 109 (Alain le Garsmeur), 114 (bottom – Roger Scruton), 122 (bottom – David Bowie), 128 (middle – Robert Hallmann). *Daniel Blatt:* 82 (bottom), 153 (right). *David Simson:* 157. *Ecoscene:* 22 (bottom right – Wayne Lawler), 32 (Ian Beames), 114 (top right – Luc Hosten), 114 (top left – Wayne Lawler), 120 (top left – Kieran Murray), 120 (bottom – Alex Bartel), 125 (top right – Erik Schaffer), 125 (middle – Platt), 125 (bottom right – Christine Osborne), 126 (top left – Nick Hawkes), 126 (top right – Peter Hulme), 126 (top middle – Andrew Brown), 126 (middle – John Farmar). *Fire Service College:* 101 (bottom). *FLPA:* 24 (bottom right – Chris Mattison), 24 (top right – Fritz Polking), 26 (left – E & D Hosking), 27 (top – Derek Middleton), 27 (bottom – P Heard), 40 (bottom left – Derek Middleton), 40 (bottom middle – F Polking), 50 (middle – Gerard Lacz), 51 (top – J Zimmermann), 53 (D P Wilson), 60 (Gerald Lacz), 65 (left – USGS R Holcomb), 82 (top – A J Roberts), 143 (bottom – Dembinsky Photo Assoc.). *Ford Motor Company:* 158 (top). *Fortean Picture Library:* 50 (bottom – Patterson/Gimlin, René Dahinden). *Garden & Wildlife Matters:* 22 (bottom left – John & Irene Palmer), 25, 38 (top – J Feltwell), 38 (middle – J Feltwell), 55 (bottom). *G.S.F. Picture Library:* 64 (top), 65 (right – Dr B Booth), 80 (bottom), 81 (top), 81 (bottom), 86 (top), 86 (middle), 96 (middle), 96 (bottom), 98 (Dr F Taylor), 123 (Dr B Booth), 132–133. *Holt Studios International:* 17 (bottom – Nigel Cattlin), 18 (top – Nigel Cattlin), 55 (middle – Wayne Hutchinson), 101 (Willem Harinck). *Jennie Woodcock:* 135. *Life File:* 66 (top – Emma Lee). *London Underground Limited:* 140. *Mary Evans Picture Library:* 6 (middle). *Medipix:* 107 (top). *Michael Brooke:* 18 (bottom), 88 (top), 102, 106 (top), 106 (bottom). *Montagu Motor Museum:* 128 (bottom right), 156. *Oxford Scientific Films:* 22 (top – Max Gibbs), 24 (bottom left – Gerald Thompson), 24 (top left – Hans Reinhard), 26 (right – Peter Parks), 50 (top – William Gray), 64 (bottom right – Joan Root), 124 (bottom – Norbert Rosing). *PA News Photo Library:* 94, 120 (top right – David Jones). *Panos Pictures:* 23 (Clive Shirley), 84 (Daniel O'Leary), 153 (left – Fred Hoogervorst). *Popperphoto:* 108, 122 (top – Reuters). *Quality Aviation Photos International:* 155 (left). *Robert Harding:* 44 (bottom). *Science & Society Picture Library:* 9 (top – Science Museum). *Science Photo Library:* 6 (top – Alexander Tsiaras), 6 (bottom – CNRI), 7 (top), 7 (bottom – Mehau Kulyk), 9 (bottom – CNRI), 10 (top right – Claude Nuridsany & Marie Perennou), 10 (bottom left – Andrew Syred), 11 (Michael Abbey), 12 (J.C. Revy), 13 (top left – Manfred Kage), 13 (top right – Pr S. Cinti/CNRI), 13 (bottom left – Dr Tony Brain), 13 (bottom right – Claude Nuridsany & Marie Perennou), 15 (top – Manfred Kage), 16 (top – Astrid and Hanns-Frieder Michler), 16 (bottom – Science Pictures Limited), 17 (top – George Bernard), 39 (Dr Yorgos Nikas), 40 (top left – Professor P.M. Motta, G. Macchiarelli, S.A. Nottola), 40 (top right – D. Phillips), 43 (Dr Yorgos Nikas), 44 (top – Petit Format/Nestle), 46 (top – Simon Fraser/Princess Mary Hospital, Newcastle), 57 (NIBSC), 92 (middle – Andrew Syred), 92 (bottom – Dr P Marazzi), 126 (bottom – Adam Hart-Davies), 143 (middle – Quest), 144 (top – BSIP VEM), 144 (middle – Adam Hart-Davis), 144 (bottom – Department of Clinical Radiology, Salisbury District Hospital), 152 (NASA), 162 (top right – NASA), 162 (top left – NASA), 162 (bottom – NASA), 163 (Frank Zullo), 164 (Bill Belnap), 167 (top – JISAS/Lockheed), 167 (bottom – NASA), 168 (top – NASA), 168 (bottom – NASA), 169 (top – Jerry Schad), 169 (bottom – G. Antonio Milani), 170 (top – US Geological Survey), 170 (bottom – NASA), 171 (top – NASA), 171 (middle – Space Telescope Science Institute/NASA), 171 (bottom – NASA), 172 (bottom – Space Telescope Science Institute/NASA). *Shout Pictures (John Callan):* 15 (bottom right), 51 (bottom), 66 (bottom), 67, 78 (top), 88 (bottom), 93 (top), 158 (bottom). *Sutton Motorsport Images:* 155 (right). *Topham Picturepoint:* 148 (top – Press Association), 148 (bottom – Press Association), 150 (Press Association).

Contents

UNIT 1 Cells

Living things are made from different parts called organs. An organ does an important job that helps the organism live. The heart, lungs and stomach are some organs in humans. Leaves are important organs in plants. They make food for the plant using energy from the Sun.

All living organisms are made of cells, which have a nucleus, and those cells are adapted for their functions.

Learning objectives ▶

Reading this unit will help you learn about and understand the following ideas and processes to do with cells:

That all plants and animals are made up of living cells which are very small.

About how microscopes are used to view small objects.

What the parts inside cells are and what they do.

About some ways in which animals and plant cells are similar.

About some ways in which animals and plant cells are different.

How specialised cells in animals and plants carry out specific roles.

That when living things grow new cells are made by cell division.

That new organisms grow from single cells.

Key words ▶

asexual reproduction	chloroplast	granule	reproduction
cell	cloning	magnification	system
cell membrane	cytoplasm	nucleus	tissue
cell wall	division	organ	vacuole
chlorophyll	gene	organisms	variation

Learning summary ▼

This table summarises the key learning points in this unit.

	Cells			Tissues — Cells of the same type			Organs — Different tissues		
	Cytoplasm	Membrane	Nucleus	Muscle	Nerve	Red blood cell (RBC)	Eye	Heart	Brain
Contain	Plant or animal	Plant or animal	Plant or animal						
Example				Muscle	Nerve	Red blood cell (RBC)	Eye	Heart	Brain
Job	Where chemical reactions take place	Lets substance in or out of the cell	Controls the cell using genes	Moves bones	Carries messages from brain and senses	Carry oxygen from the lungs to cells	Collects visual data	Pumps blood around the body	Controls body
Plants also contain	Cell wall	Vacuole	Chloroplasts	Palisade	Root	Stem			
Job of these are:	To support the cell	To support the cell	To make food						
Special feature	Nerve	RBC	Muscle	Palisade	Roots		Skin		
	Long with connections to many other cells	Losses nucleus so it can carry more	Can shorten quickly	Lots of chloroplasts	Hairs to increase surface area				
Job	See tissues	See tissues	See tissues	Making food by photosynthesis	Absorbs water and minerals				
Division	See flow chart below			Growth by cell division			Growth by cell division		

Cell division to make identical cells

Start → Nucleus is copied → Nucleus divides into two → New nuclear membrane grows → Cytoplasm divides → Stop

Two identical cells made

| This type of division is found in asexual reproduction | | | | Plant tissue culture produced lots of new identical plants from cells |
| Uses of cloning | | | | Animal tissue e.g. skin to repair damage due to an accident |

Use tables to make a summary of other units.

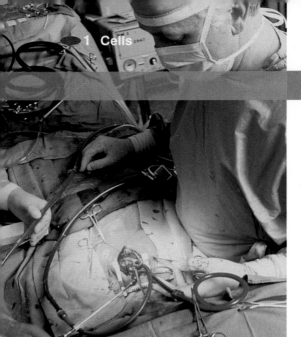

1.1 *Replacing a faulty heart valve*

Looking inside the body

When things go wrong with our bodies, we visit a doctor for help. Doctors have spent many years learning about the body. They know how the body is made and how it works. They understand how each **organ** in the body works to keep us alive. They can even replace faulty organs, sometimes with artificial ones. In the picture on the left, doctors are repairing a faulty heart valve.

In the past doctors made observations to discover how the body works. They cut up the bodies of animals and people who had died. They discovered the different organs that make up a body. In some countries this was very dangerous because it was against the law to cut up human bodies – even if they were already dead!

1 Make a list of all of the organs in the body that you know.

2 What jobs do these organs do?

1.2 *Early anatomists in action*

1.3 *X-ray showing bones in the hand*

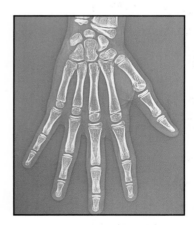

Doctors carried out experiments to find out how the organs worked. Sometimes they used soldiers who had been injured in battle for their experiments. Because of their wounds their internal organs were often visible and doctors could investigate what these organs did.

Modern doctors do not always have to cut open a body to look inside. They can look inside the body in many different ways. Scientists have invented machines and computers to help us to see inside.

X-rays can pass through the soft parts of bodies. But the bones inside our bodies do not let X -rays pass through. They show up as light in an X-ray picture. This picture shows the bones in a hand.

The stomach cannot normally be seen with X-rays. This picture was taken after a patient had a drink containing a substance that shows up on X-rays.

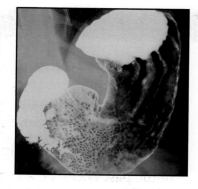

1.4 *X-ray showing the stomach after a barium meal*

3 Why can we not normally see the stomach in an X-ray?

Even more detailed pictures of the body can be made using a scan. In this picture we can see the brain and other organs inside the head.

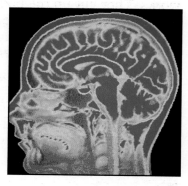

1.5 *A scan of a human head, showing the brain*

4 Why do you think different colours are used in the scan picture?

Most living things are made up from parts called organs, which carry out important jobs. The different organs work together to keep the body alive. To help them work well together, organs with related jobs are often connected to each other to make up a **system**.

Plants are much simpler than animals, but they are made up of different organs too.

5 Which of the organs in picture 1.6 form part of the digestive system?

6 What jobs do the plant organs in picture 1.7 do?

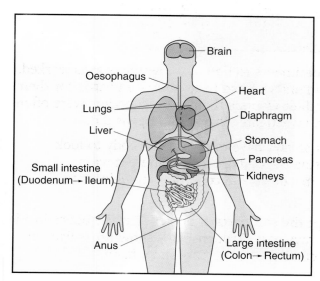

Brain
Oesophagus
Heart
Lungs
Diaphragm
Liver
Stomach
Pancreas
Small intestine (Duodenum → Ileum)
Kidneys
Anus
Large intestine (Colon → Rectum)

1.6 *Some major organs of the body*

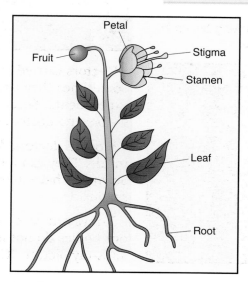

Petal
Fruit
Stigma
Stamen
Leaf
Root

1.7 *Some important plant organs*

Microscopes and magnification

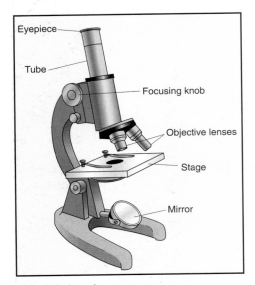

1.8 *A light microscope*

Doctors and scientists often use a microscope to look more closely at living things.

A microscope magnifies objects. It makes them seem much bigger than in real life so we can see in more detail what they are like. A microscope uses two lenses to **magnify** the image of the object being viewed. A knob on the side is used to move the object into the correct position for us to see a clear, magnified image. School microscopes magnify objects between 40 and 400 times.

The **magnification** tells you how much bigger the object looks.

×10 means 10 times bigger

×40 means 40 times bigger

×100 means 100 times bigger

Often objects viewed with a microscope look very different from how we imagine them to be. These pictures show common objects viewed through a microscope.

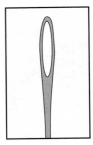

1.9 *Actual size: 3 mm*

1.10 *Actual size: 2 mm*

7 What do you think the objects in the pictures might be?

1.11 *Actual size: 34 mm*

8 Work out the magnification of the objects in the pictures.

You can work out the magnification of an object using this formula:

$$\frac{\text{Size of magnified object}}{\text{Size of real object}} = \text{magnification}$$

HISTORY BOX

A new way of looking

When the microscope was invented in around 1600, it gave scientists a new way of looking at things. They could see things that nobody had ever been able to look at before.

Robert Hooke, an English inventor and scientist, wanted to find out more about how living things were made. He used a microscope to look more closely at things. He prepared microscope slides of different things to observe. He looked closely at different parts of plants and animals. One of his specimens was a thin piece of cork taken from just under the bark of a tree.

Hooke carefully recorded his observations by making a drawing of the cork. He described what he saw. He said the cork seemed to be made from hundreds of tiny boxes. These made it look a bit like a honeycomb.

He called these little boxes **cells**. He thought that they made a kind of skeleton inside the plant.

1.12 *Hooke's microscope*

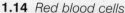

1.13 *Hooke's first drawing of cork cells*

9 How is Hooke's microscope different from the one you use at school?

10 Why do you think Hooke called the objects he saw 'cells'?

1.14 *Red blood cells*

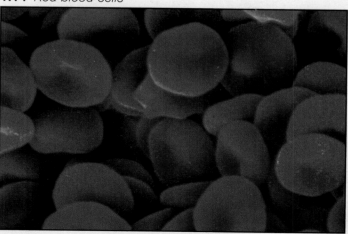

Around the same time, a Dutchman called Jan Swammerdam was looking at blood through a microscope. He saw tiny round objects floating in the blood. These were cells too.

Scientists looked at more and more living things under the microscope. They soon realised that nearly all living things were made up from cells.

This was a revolutionary change in how scientists viewed living things. But it was many years before they realised how important cells were. Hooke simply thought that the cells he saw were part of the skeleton of a plant. He did not believe that they were living.

It took nearly 200 years for scientists to understand that the cells in living things were alive.

The units of life

Over the last 200 years we have come to realise just how important Hooke's observations were. All living things are made up of these tiny units, which can only be seen using a microscope. All of the processes of life go on inside cells.

A human is made up of about 50 million, million cells. Each cell is very, very small, but it is alive.

Each cell *needs a supply of food* to provide it with energy. It needs *oxygen* to help get energy from food. The energy is used for *moving,* and *growing* and making new substances. Some of the substances made in cells are poisonous and must be removed (*excreted*) from the cell. Cells are *sensitive* to things going on in their environment. All of these life processes go on inside cells in plants and animals.

Using a microscope we can see more clearly what cells look like. The cells of animals and plants contain many parts which are the same. But there are differences between them. The cells are usually stained with a chemical before being observed. This makes some of the parts inside the cell easier to see.

These pictures show what cells from the skin of an onion look like when viewed through a microscope. Using high magnification we can see what is inside the cell.

11 Why do you think cells are so small?

12 Make a list of the life processes that go on inside cells. Explain why each is important.

13 How might the cells in the middle of your brain get the substances they need to keep alive?

1.15 *A cross-section through an onion*

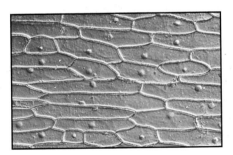

1.16 *Onion skin, low magnification*

14 Why are cells stained before we look at them through a microscope?

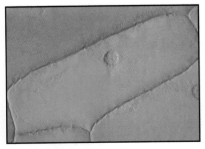

1.17 *Onion skin cell, high magnification*

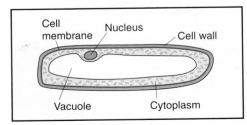

1.18 *An onion skin cell*

Cell membrane Nucleus Cell wall
Vacuole Cytoplasm

Inside an animal cell

A typical animal cell has a simple structure when seen through a microscope. It consists of **cytoplasm** surrounded by a thin **cell membrane** and, in most cells, a **nucleus**.

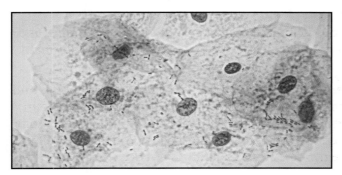

1.19 *Cheek lining cells*

Most of the inside of the cell is made up of **cytoplasm**. This is a jelly-like substance. Many important chemical reactions go on in this part of the cell. Some of these reactions release energy, which keeps the cell alive. If you look at cytoplasm carefully, you may see tiny bits inside it. Some of these **granules** are stores of food inside the cell.

The **cell membrane** forms a kind of skin around the cytoplasm. The membrane is very thin. It controls what enters and leaves the cell. Substances that the cell needs, such as oxygen and food, pass into the cell through this membrane. Some substances that the cell makes pass out of the cell through the membrane.

The **nucleus** is a round blob seen inside most cells. It acts as a control centre for the cell, controlling many of the processes going on inside the cell, how the cell develops and what it does. The instructions that control how the cell develops and works are called **genes**. They are inside the nucleus.

15 Why do cells need a store of food?

16 Why is the cell membrane so thin?

17 Make a list of the parts inside an animal cell. Write down what each part does.

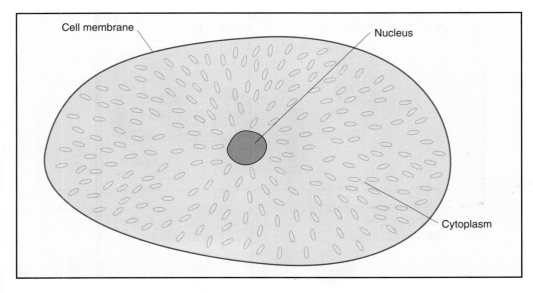

1.20 *Inside a typical animal cell*

Inside a plant cell

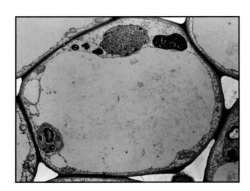

1.21 *A moss leaf cell*

Plants are made from living cells too. Plant cells have the same parts as animal cells. They have a cell membrane, a nucleus and are filled with cytoplasm. However, they have extra parts, which are only found in plant cells.

All plant cells have a **cell wall**, which surrounds the membrane, and a **vacuole** filled with a watery sap. Some plant cells also contain many green discs called **chloroplasts**.

The cell wall surrounds the membrane. It is much thicker and tougher than the membrane. It is made from a substance called **cellulose**. This is an important substance for mankind. Many everyday products, such as paper, are made from cellulose. The cellulose cell wall is strong. It helps the plant cell to keep its shape.

Inside the cell wall, the plant cell is made of cytoplasm, surrounded by a thin cell membrane.

The vacuole is a large space inside the cytoplasm. It is filled with a watery fluid containing sugars and salt. The vacuole helps to make plant cells firm, and this helps to support the plant. This is why most plants feel quite hard when touched.

Chloroplasts are only found in cells in the green parts of plants, such as the leaves and stems. They are important in making food for the plant. Chloroplasts contain a green substance called **chlorophyll**. This is why the leaves and stems of many plants look green. This is the substance that absorbs light energy to help plants make food.

18 Make a list of the parts inside an plant cell. Write down what each part does.

19 How are plant cells similar to, and different from, animal cells?

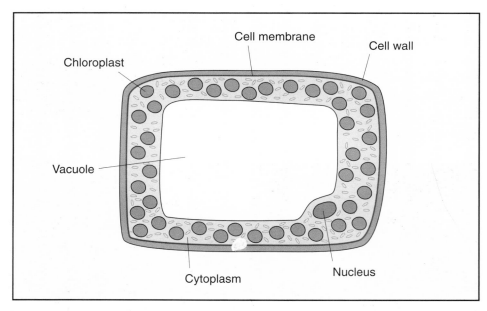

1.22 *Inside a typical plant cell*

Find out more about a plant cell at ▶ **www.scienceweb.co.uk**

Different types of cells

There are many different types of cells in animals and plants. Each type of cell has a particular job to do. Each has its own special shape and structure. This helps it to carry out its role properly.

Nerve cells carry electrical messages around the body. They are long and thin, and make connections with other cells.

Muscle cells can shorten suddenly, and cause muscles to move parts of the body.

Red cells in the blood carry oxygen around the body to other cells which need it. They are thin and flexible so they can travel in the blood more easily. They are filled with a chemical which attracts oxygen. They have no nucleus, to make more room for this chemical.

In plants, palisade cells in the leaves contain many chloroplasts, and carry out photosynthesis, making food for the plant.

Cells in the roots do not have chloroplasts. They cannot make food. They carry out the important job of taking up water and minerals from the soil. Some of these cells have a long thin extension which takes in water from the soil. These are called root hair cells.

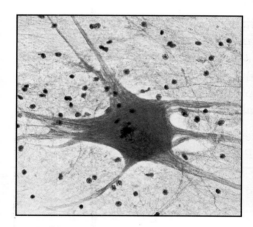

1.23 *Nerve cell*

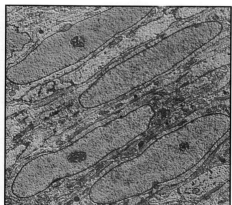

1.24 *Muscle cells*

1.25 *Red blood cells*

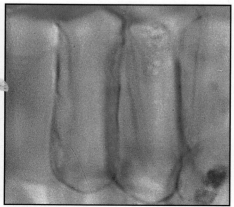

1.26 *Palisade leaf cells*

20 Make a line drawing of a single example of each of these cells. Label the parts of the cell which you can see.

21 Which cells come from plants? What are the differences?

13

Building living things

1.27 *Cells mass together to make tissue, rather like bricks forming a wall*

Most living things are made of millions of cells. The cells are not just mixed together. Cells of the same type are collected together in large groups. A group of cells of the same type is called a **tissue**.

This is a bit like how the wall of a house is made from many bricks. The wall is like a tissue of brick 'cells'. Just like the house is made from different types of raw materials, a living thing is made from different types of tissues.

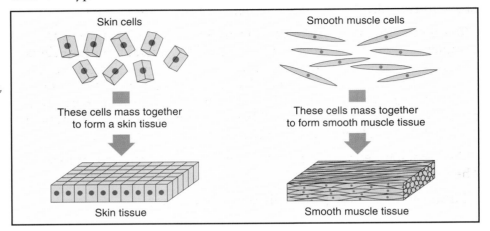

1.28 *How cells of one type form a tissue*

22 How is a wall similar to a tissue?

23 Why are cells of one type grouped together to form tissues?

Millions of cells of the same type can work more effectively in a tissue than if they are mixed up with other cells. When millions of muscle cells are grouped together to make muscle tissue, they can move the bones in your legs and make you run! A single muscle cell could never do this.

Each organ in the body is made up from different types of tissue.

24 How can you tell the difference between different tissues?

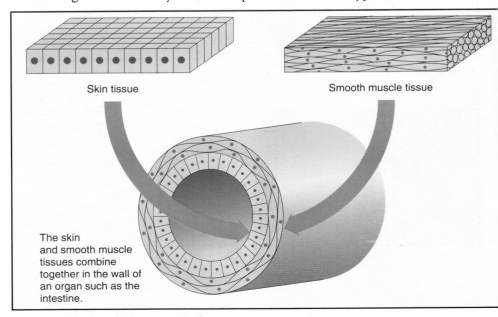

The skin and smooth muscle tissues combine together in the wall of an organ such as the intestine.

1.29 *How different tissues form an organ*

Making new cells

When an animal or plant grows it gets larger. Living things grow by making new cells. The new cells are made by cell **division**. This happens when acell divides. Each time a cell divides two new cells are made.

Before a cell divides, the nucleus makes a copy of itself. A copy is made of each of the genes inside the nucleus. These will provide each new cell with the information it needs for it to live and work. The next problem is to divide the genes up between the two new cells.

To do this, the nucleus divides so that each new cell can get one complete set of instructions. Two new nuclei are made. Each nucleus contains the instructions for controlling one cell. A new membrane grows between the two new cells. These are often called 'daughter cells'. They are smaller than a fully grown cell of the same kind. The cytoplasm of the parent is shared between the daughter cells. In plant cells, a new bit of cell wall also grows around each new cell.

The two new cells both grow again until they reach their full size. Then each one divides again.

These pictures show plant cells that are dividing.

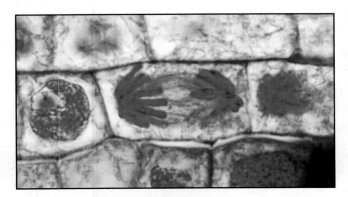

1.30 *Actively dividing cells; nuclear division can be seen*

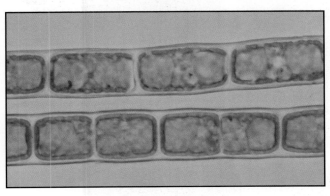

1.31 *An actively dividing cell from a filamentous alga; differences in cell size can be seen*

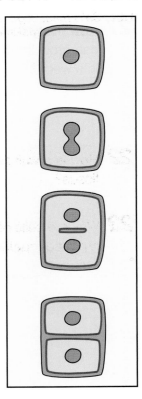

1.32 *Different stages of cell division in a plant cell*

25 What evidence is there in pictures 1.30 and 1.31 that some cells are dividing?

Find out more about cell division at ▶ **www.scienceweb.co.uk**

Making new individuals

In many living organisms new individuals can be made when cells from a parent break off and begin to divide and grow. This is called **asexual reproduction**, because only one parent is needed. The advantage is that there is no variation and the young are identical to the adult.

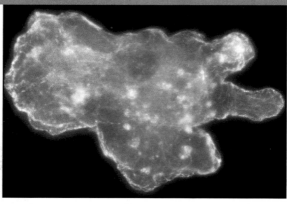

1.33 *An amoeba*

> **26** Make a flowchart to show how an *amoeba* divides.

> **27** How many new individuals can grow from one *amoeba* in a week?

An *amoeba* is a living thing made up of only one cell. It lives in ponds, feeding on bits of decaying matter and bacteria. An *amoeba* reproduces simply by splitting in two. The process is just like cell division. First the nucleus divides and then the cell splits across the middle. The two new *amoebas* feed and grow. After about 24 hours each divides again.

In some larger animals, a new individual can grow from cells in the body of the parent. A *hydra* is a small animal which lives in ponds. A young *hydra* grows as a bud on the side of the parent's body. The bud is made by a special cell which divides over and over again. As the bud grows, the cells rearrange themselves to make the young *hydra*. When it is big enough, it breaks away from the parent and lives by itself.

1.34 *Budding in hydra*

Many plants can be grown from **cuttings**. A small part of the plant, usually a piece of stem or root is cut off the parent plant. When the cutting is planted in soil, a new plant grows. The cells in the cutting divide and make many new cells. The new cells change. They grow to make new tissues and organs.

Bulbs of daffodils, tulips and iris are planted each year in the garden and new plants grow from them. Gardeners prefer to collect the flowers for decoration and let the plant produce new plants by letting the old bulb produce a number of new bulbs. The bulb is a swollen leaf bud and if you cut through one you can see the different layers that make up the leaf bud. The layers are swollen with food and act as a food store for the new plant. In this way gardeners guarantee getting the same type of flower each year.

1.35 *A sprouting bulb*

Other plants like potatoes use swollen underground stems called **tubers**. Each plant will produce a number of new tubers that will each grow into a new plant.

One strange plant called the 'good luck plant' produces small plants on the edges of its leaves. Each new plant has grown from special cells on the edge of the leaf. These small plants fall off onto the soil below and root and eventually grow into large plants.

In asexual reproduction there is only one parent producing new organisms. The advantage of asexual reproduction is there is no **variation** so new young organisms are identical to an adult. Gardeners make use of asexual reproduction to reproduce plants from year to year. In this way they can guarantee getting the same type of flower each year.

28 Why would gardeners want to produce the same type of plant each year?

29 What are the advantages of asexual reproduction?

1.36 *A sprouting potato tuber*

TECHNOLOGY BOX

1.37 *Cauliflower clones in a test tube*

Using cells

The genetic information inside the cell's nucleus contains all of the instructions needed to grow a new individual. Scientists have been able to find ways of making new individuals which are identical copies of the parent. This process is called **cloning**.

Simple tissue culture in plants

Tissue culture is widely used to produce genetically identical copies of plants (**clones**). Scientists choose the most productive or decorative plant and copy it many times. This is quicker and more reliable than letting plants reproduce by making seeds. It can make more plants than asexual reproduction.

The process starts with a small cutting. It can be taken from any part of the plant, since all the plant's cells contain the genetic information from which an entire plant can be grown. The small cutting is placed in a culture medium, a mixture of nutrients that supplies all its needs. The mixture includes a special growth substance to stimulate the cells in the cutting to divide and produce a mass of plant cells that divide rapidly. As this mass of cells grows and divides, the cells begin to change. They make the different cells and tissues of the new young plant.

The cauliflower plants in the photograph have been grown in this way. Potato and tomato plants can also be produced quickly using tissue cultures.

Growing animal tissues

1.38 *Animal tissue culture in a Petri dish*

Animals are not so easy to clone. Once cells have become specialised, for example as skin cells, they will only make other cells of the same type when they divide. They will not produce a new individual.

This can be useful, however. Scientists can now grow many types of human cell in cultures outside the body. These artificial tissues can be used to investigate cells. This will make it possible to grow replacement tissue such as skin to repair skin damaged in accidents.

The most recent advances in science involve looking for ways to grow whole individuals from single animal cells. Some scientists in Scotland have grown a sheep called Dolly from a single cell.

Questions

1 Here are two pictures of cells.

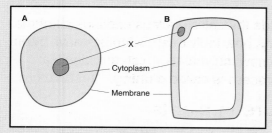

  a Which cell is a plant cell?
  b Why is that cell a plant cell?
  c What is part X in both cells?

2 The cell has a number of different parts and each part is involved in a different function. Complete the following table indicating the part of the cell involved in the function named.

Cell function	Cell part
a This cell part helps the cell to keep its shape	
b This cell part is where the chemical reactions take place	
c This cell part controls the cell and its activities	
d This cell part is important for making food in plant cells	
e This cell part controls the substances entering and leaving the cell	

3 The following cells are found in different tissues in different animal organs. Identify the cells and the organ systems in which they are found.

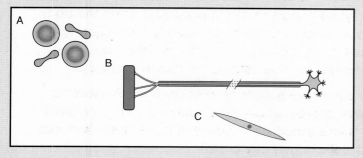

4 Name the part of the cell that contains the information needed to make a new organism.

5 Label this diagram of a plant cell.

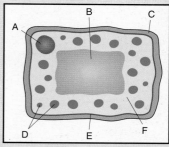

6 Living organisms are made up of many similar units organised into special structures. Complete the following diagram showing the relationship between different structures in the organism.

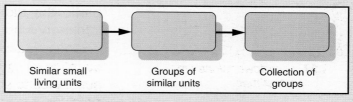

7 When a single cell reproduces by splitting it is called ....

8 Complete the following passage by filling in the missing words.

Plant and animal cells have a jelly-like material called the .... in which there are different cell structures. It is in this jelly-like substance that chemical reactions take place. This jelly-like substance is surrounded by the .... In plants this is found under the .... One of the cell structures in plants contains a green substance that helps to produce sugar in photosynthesis. This is called a .... In all plant and animal cells there is a large structure called the .... that controls all that happens in the cell. In plant cells there is a space called the .... which contains sugar and salts.

9 Give one advantage and one disadvantage of asexual reproduction.

10 What scientific instrument would you use to look at a cell? What two lenses would you need to get an instrument that magnifies a cell 300 times?

The environment and

The place where animals and plants live is called a habitat. Different habitats provide homes for different types of living thing. The living things are adapted to survive in the particular habitat they live in. They have special features to help them survive in their habitat.

Some of the animals in a habitat feed on the plants living there. Some animals feed on other animals. A food chain diagram represents how food is passed from one living thing to another when they eat.

Reading this unit will help you to know about and understand the following ideas and processes to do with living things in the environment:

About ways in which habitats vary and how this affects the animals and plants that live in them.

How plants and animals are adapted to live in a particular habitat.

Some ways in which plants and animals interact with their environment and with each other, including feeding relationships.

About how living things are adapted to survive winter conditions.

That food chains may be linked to form food webs which show what different animals feed on.

That energy is passed from one living thing to another in a food chain.

About the effects on a food web of changing the numbers of one type of living thing in it.

adaptation	dormant	herbivores	primary consumer
adapted	ecosystem	hibernate	producers
biosphere	environment	migrate	quadrat
carnivores	food chain	omnivores	secondary consumer
community	food pyramid	predator	
consumer	food web	prey	transect
decomposers	habitat		

feeding relationships

Learning summary ▽

These flashcards summarise the key learning points in this unit.

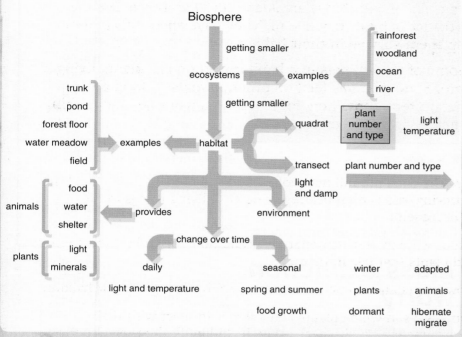

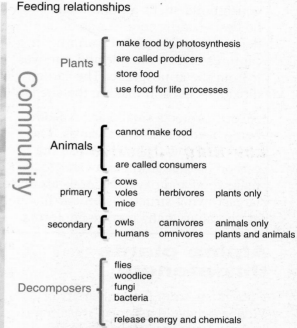

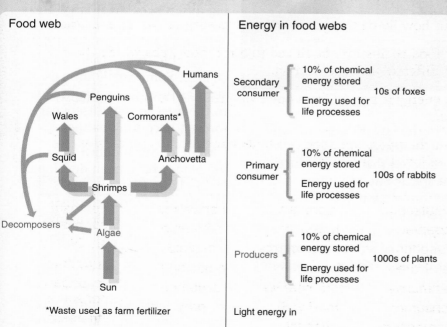

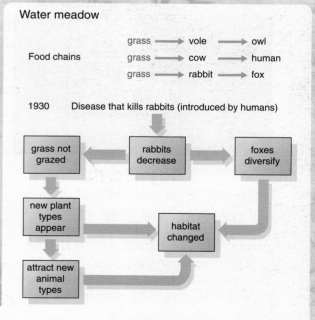

Use flashcards like these to make a summary of another unit.

Ecology Echo

CRISIS IN CORAL BEAUTY SPOT

Coral reefs are made from the bodies of millions of tiny animals, which build shells around their bodies. Healthy coral is one of our defences against global warming. It captures carbon dioxide and removes it from the atmosphere. The carbon dioxide is used in making the shells.

Coral protects small islands from being beaten by the sea waves. The coral feeds on algae which use the carbon dioxide in the seawater to make food and oxygen. Corals are the largest living structures on Earth and are home to many marine life forms.

2.1 *Coral*

The coral around many of our islands is disappearing because of pollution and fishing. Coral reefs form where the water temperature is 20–29°C. This is also the region where 60% of the world's population wants to live. People remove soil to make way for homes, and the soil flows into the sea and suffocates the coral. In other areas coral is used as building material. In some areas fishermen overfish the coral reefs and upset the balance of life forms. They even use dynamite to catch fish, and the explosions damage the coral.

Alpine plants threatened

Scientists from the University of Vienna believe that global warming is making some rare alpine flowers extinct.

2.2 *Alpine flowers*

The Alps were a cool place but global warming has changed that and the rise in temperature has favoured some plants that like warmer climates. The competition is so fierce that some of the beautiful alpine plants in this once cool community are becoming extinct.

In the 1960s Rachel Carson predicted the extinction of species because of human activity. Now her predictions seem to be coming true.

Mass extinction worry

2.3 *Mining in the rainforest*

In the late 1950s and early 1960s Edward O. Wilson predicted the mass extinction of species due to human action. Now it seems his predictions are coming true in tropical regions. In Brazil millions of square kilometres of tropical rainforest are being cut down each year. The land is being used for mining and for building new cities and roads.

Chopping down parts of the rainforest means new plant species move in, taking over from the older plants. In small amounts this does not make a big difference, but if large areas are cut down the forest will change and the number of living things able to live there will change. Some small animals such as insects may be unique to the area so they disappear forever, becoming extinct.

Many of our modern medicines have been developed from plants found in the rainforests. Some scientists believe that there are many more important discoveries to be made there. If the forests disappear, we may never find the cure for some illnesses. Governments around the world are in talks with Brazil to find a way to halt the destruction.

1 Why would the alpine plants change if the weather becomes warmer?

2 What could be done to save the rainforest?

El Niño *destroys local food chains*

Roberto lives on the coast of Peru and lives by fishing. The past years have been good, with many fish caught. The family has eaten some of these fish but most have been sold to feed others. This year it is different.

Ocean currents flow past the coast of Peru. This cold current of water brings nutrients from the water of the Antarctic. From the cool deep water of the Antarctic minerals pass into the waters of the Pacific. Tiny plants called algae use sunlight to make food by photosynthesis. The algae also use the mineral salts to help them grow and be healthy.

El Niño is the name given to a current of warm water which sometimes flows towards the coasts of Chile and Peru. This warm water does not carry as many minerals as the normal cold water. Without these minerals the algae cannot grow and use photosynthesis to make food.

In 1998 El Niño came towards the coast. It caused the sea temperature to rise above 30°C and this killed the algae. The algae are food to shrimps and many small fish. The shrimps are food for squid and fish called anchovetta. The fishermen catch the squid and fish to feed other people in their towns, villages and cities.

2.4 *Fishermen from Peru fishing in the Pacific*

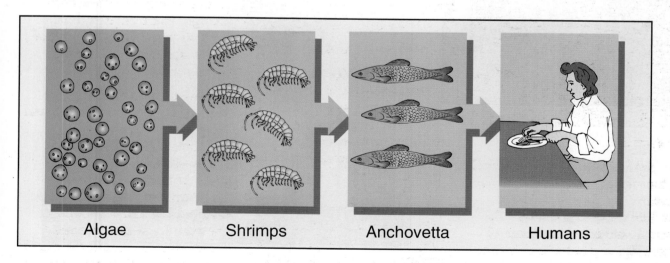

| Algae | Shrimps | Anchovetta | Humans |

The fishermen and their families belong to small communities. The fish are caught and bought and sold by members of the community. In this way, the money that changes hands within a community is linked to the catch of fish.

3 What do the arrows in a food chain diagram represent?

Habitats

The living part of our world is the **biosphere**. In this biosphere all living things depend upon each other. To look at this dependence is difficult so scientists break the whole biosphere down into small units, which have a common set of plants or animals. These are called **ecosystems** and are often large areas like tropical rainforests, woodlands, rivers, oceans, etc.

Even an ecosystem is too large to study because there are so many living organisms involved. In the ecosystem there are smaller groups of living things, which live in a smaller area and are dependent upon each other. This is called a **habitat** such as a field or meadow, pond, marsh, tree trunk or forest floor, etc.

2.5 *Different habitats (clockwise): stream, tree trunk, meadow and pond*

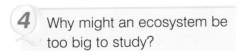

4 Why might an ecosystem be too big to study?

5 What animals and plants might you find in each ecosystem pictured?

For most living things their habitat is the area in which they live. The habitat provides animals and plants with the things they need to survive, such as food, water, shelter, light and minerals. What a habitat is like is called its **environment**. Different habitats have different environments.

Investigating habitats

Each habitat provides a home for a **community** of living things. The community of animals and plants in each type of habitat is different because the environments are different. The living things in each type of habitat have features to help them survive in a particular environment. These features are called **adaptations**. We say that the living things are **adapted** to the environment in their habitat.

Animals and plants living in different habitats have to be good at surviving in different conditions. So we find different types of animals and plants in each habitat.

2.6 *Water meadow*

A group of children decided to investigate a water meadow habitat. Jody and Ann compared the plants growing in two areas of the meadow. One area was by the forest edge, the other was by the side of the river.

To make the comparison a fair one, they measured out 1 m² of ground at each site. The measured area is called a **quadrat**. The children measured the numbers and types of plants at each site, and recorded the temperature and amount of light 10 cm above the ground. They recorded their observations carefully.

When they compared the two sites in the meadow they had several questions to think about.

6 Why do different plants grow close to the trees compared with the side of the river?

7 Is it light or temperature that affects the growth of plants?

8 Why do some plants have lots of leaves and others only have a few?

Jo and Ali drew a cross section of the meadow. This cross section of a habitat is called a **transect**. They wanted to know whether the conditions in the environment affected how plants grow. They moved across the field in a straight line recording the different species of plant growing, the temperature near the ground and how damp the ground was.

Jo and Ali had a few questions on their mind when they looked at their results.

9 Why does the height of plants change along the line from the forest to the river?

10 What causes different types of plant to grow across the meadow?

11 Why do small plants grow under trees?

Changing environments

Habitats can change over time. Cutting down large areas of a rainforest, and hunting or burning to clear the land can change an environment drastically and lead to the extinction of living things. Natural events, like El Niño, or a large-scale flood, can make changes in the living organisms in a community.

Not all changes are dangerous, however. The environment of a habitat is changing all the time. Some of these changes are small and occur on a daily basis. Other changes take place over a longer period, with the changing seasons.

Daily changes

Every 24 hours the Sun rises, passes across the sky, and sets. The graph shows how the amount of light in a habitat changes during 1 day.

Living things are controlled by the changes in their environment.

During the day, when it is light, many animals stay under cover. Some animals, like woodlice, prefer the cooler, damper conditions at night. Their bodies would dry up if they came out on a warm sunny day. Other animals stay under cover during the day to hide from **predators**. It is safer for mice and voles to feed in the dusk and early morning.

Owls are predators. They have adaptations to help them to catch other animals, such as mice, which are their **prey**.

Many insects, such as butterflies and bees, are most active during daylight hours. They feed on nectar from flowers which are only open during the day. They need to be warmed by the Sun so that they can fly. Most moths only fly at night. During the day they hide from predators. They are camouflaged so that they can hide in their habitat during the day.

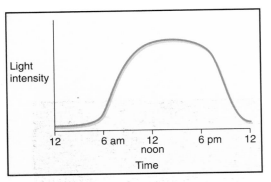

2.7 *Changes in light intensity over 1 day*

12 Describe the pattern in this graph.

13 Draw a graph to show how the temperature will change over 24 hours.

14 How are owls adapted to be good hunters?

2.8 *A barn owl*

2.9 *A peppered moth on a tree trunk*

Seasonal changes

During the course of a year, the environment in a habitat can change greatly. These changes occur in the cycle of the seasons, caused by the movement of the Earth around the Sun. The changes are predictable and many organisms are adapted to survive the changes that take place.

Spring and summer are times for growth and reproduction. Plants grow well in the warm, light conditions. They make extra food which they store in seeds or other parts of the plant. There is plenty of food for animals. Most animals produce their young during this time of year.

During the winter life is harder. It is cold and there are fewer hours of sunlight each day. Plants cannot make food in these conditions. Some plants cannot survive at all. They die and only their seeds are left in the ground to germinate and grow into new plants next year.

Other plants can survive the harsh conditions of winter. They are adapted to cope with the cold winter environment. Many become **dormant**. They survive underground and the stem and leaves above the ground die off. Under the ground the plant has food stored in a swollen stem or root, or at the base of its leaves

Some plants, such as trees and bushes, lose their leaves during the winter.

Animals find winter a difficult time too. Food is hard to find and it is often of poor quality. Because it is cold they risk losing body heat and dying.

Some animals, such as the dormouse, **hibernate**. They store fat inside their bodies to provide energy during the winter. As winter approaches they build a nest in which they go into a deep sleep lasting for months. During this time, they do not use much energy because they are not moving around. They survive on their store of fat until spring comes. Many insects survive the winter as pupae which hatch out into adults in the spring.

Other animals need to find food even during the winter months and must move around to do so. The rabbit grows a thicker coat of fur to keep it warm during the winter. In spring, when it gets warmer, the animal moults and loses its extra fur.

Many birds, like swallows, **migrate** to warmer countries where there is more food available during the winter months.

15 How does losing their leaves help plants to survive the winter?

2.10 *Hibernating dormouse*

2.11 *Migrating birds*

16 Why is more food available for birds in warmer countries than Britain during the winter?

Feeding relationships and energy transfer

In the water meadow, green plants make their own food. They take in carbon dioxide from the atmosphere and water from the soil. They use the energy from sunlight to turn these into sugar for food. They release oxygen as a waste product. Plants are the source of the things animals need to survive. Plants are called **producers** because they make their own food.

Animals cannot make their own food. They must get their food by eating other living things. Animals are called **consumers**.

In the water meadow, cows and small animals such as voles and mice feed on the grass and plants in the field. They are plant eaters or **herbivores**. They digest the plants and transfer energy from the plant to their own bodies. They are called **primary consumers** because they are the first in the chain transferring energy from plants to other living things.

Owls frequently spot the small voles and mice and swoop down and catch these small animals. The owl eats the vole for food. Owls are called **carnivores** because they eat other animals. Because the owl eats the vole, which is the primary consumer, the owl is known as the **secondary consumer**. It is second in the chain transferring energy from plants to other living things. Humans are also secondary consumers because they eat the beef from the cow, the primary consumer. Humans also eat plants so they are called **omnivores**.

When an animal eats it transfers some of the energy from its food into its body. It uses some of the energy for movement and living processes. Some energy is transferred to the environment in the form of heat. This energy is unusable.

We can show how energy is passed through the living things in a habitat using a **food chain** diagram. In a food chain the arrow shows the direction in which energy is being passed.

17 Why does a food chain usually begin with a plant?

18 Which is the producer and which is the primary consumer in the two food chains in the picture?

2.12 *Two examples of a food chain*

When living things die, their bodies are broken down into chemicals and energy by other small creatures and organisms like flies, woodlice, fungi and bacteria. These are called **decomposers**. Decomposers move chemicals and energy from the bodies of dead plants and animals to living plants and animals.

The plants growing in the water meadow feed the animals which eventually feed insects and other organisms. All of the living things in a **community** depend upon each other for food and energy.

19 Why are decomposers important for food cycles?

Food webs

When an animal dies, flies and other organisms feed on the body and the energy is transferred into a different food chain. This will link two food chains together. When an animal, like the vole, is eaten by more than one kind of animal two food chains are joined together. This makes a more complicated set of joined food chains called a **food web**.

In the example of the Pacific fishermen of Peru (page 23), the food web would start with the Sun. The Sun provides the energy for the algae to produce food. Small animals such as shrimps feed on the algae. The shrimps are in turn eaten by squid, anchovetta and whales. Sperm whales, penguins and cormorants eat the squid. Cormorants, penguins and humans eat the anchovetta. Nutrients from food, minerals and energy are transferred through the different food chains. The cormorants produce waste that is collected by humans and spread on fields as guano or fertilisers to feed crops. Dead animals are fed on by decomposing bacteria that are eaten by small animals. In this way energy and chemicals like nitrogen, carbon, phosphates and minerals are **recycled**.

20 What are the producers and consumers of this food web?

21 How many different food chains can you find in this food web? Copy them out.

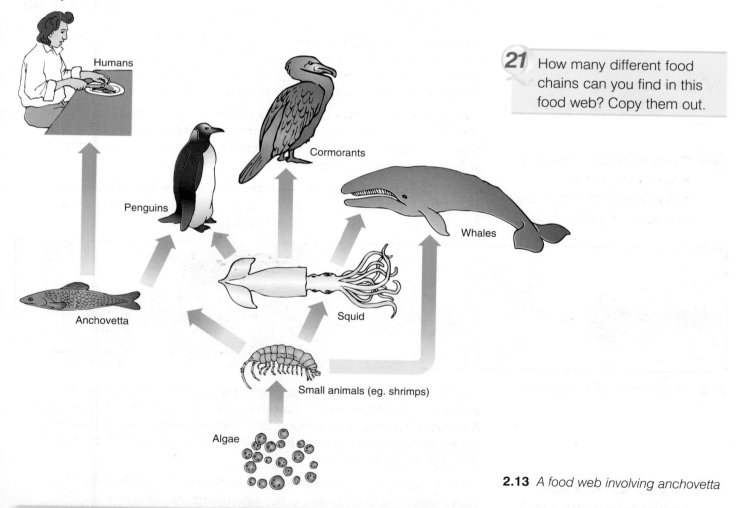

Humans

Cormorants

Penguins

Whales

Anchovetta

Squid

Small animals (eg. shrimps)

Algae

2.13 *A food web involving anchovetta*

Explore other food webs on the Internet at ▶ **www.scienceweb.co.uk**

Energy in food webs

When plants make food by photosynthesis, only some of the energy they absorb from the Sun is stored in the plant. The rest is used by the plant in its own life processes. Animals also use some of the energy from the food they eat to stay alive. So the amount of energy passed on gets smaller as it passes along the chain.

Each organism in the food chain keeps about 10% of the energy it receives as energy stored in chemicals in their body. This 10% is the energy available for the next organism in the chain. Both plants and animals lose energy as heat when they respire. Animals also lose energy when they get rid of waste and when they move. This loss of energy makes the chain short and most food chains have only four to five links.

22 What happens to the size of animals as you move along a food chain?

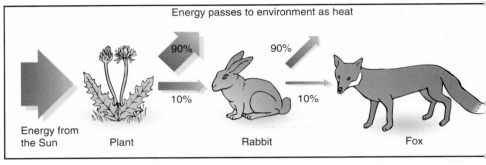

2.14 *Energy losses in a food chain*

Because energy is lost at each level of the food chain, there are usually fewer organisms at each level. A **food pyramid** shows this. Each level of the pyramid represents the numbers of organisms. There are fewer primary consumers than there are plants. There are fewer secondary consumers than primary consumers.

2.15 *A food pyramid*

23 Why do the numbers change at each level in a food pyramid?

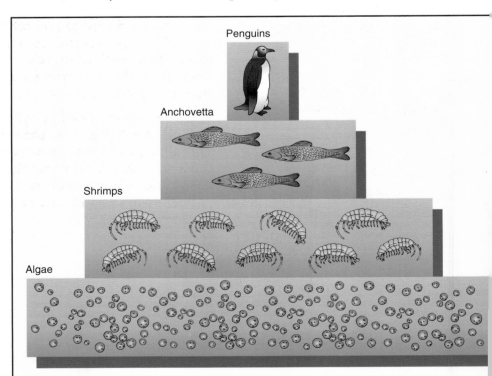

Changes in food webs

All of the living things involved in a food web depend upon each other to stay alive. If something happens to reduce the number of organisms in one part of the web, all others will be affected. It is often difficult to predict what the exact effects will be.

Here is a simple food web showing some of the animals in the British countryside. Rabbits are a main source of food for the fox population. The rabbits feed on grasses and plants growing in the meadows, heaths and downs of the countryside. Because there are so many rabbits, plants are heavily grazed and kept very short. Only plants that can withstand heavy grazing survive.

During the 1930s a disease caused by a virus attacked the Britain's rabbits. Millions died. Because there were fewer rabbits, there was less food for foxes.

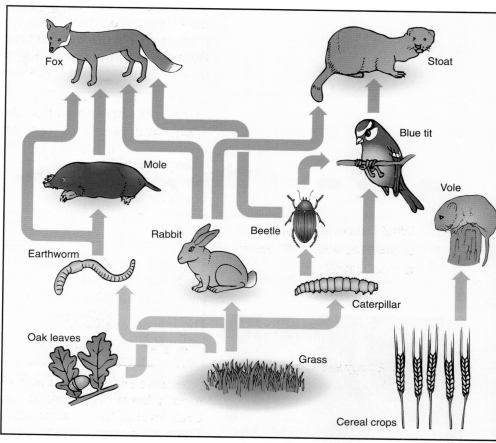

2.16 *A food web including foxes*

24 What do you think would happen to the number of foxes if there was less food for them?

25 How did the plants change when there were fewer rabbits?

26 Was the death of the rabbits a good or a bad thing? Explain your view.

Foxes were forced to find other sources of food. They began to attack farm animals such as hens and young lambs more often and to eat other small mammals. As the foxes' food changed, the numbers of these animals began to change as well. Foxes also started to move into towns to take scraps from dustbins.

Another effect of rabbits dying was that there were fewer animals feeding on the grasses in the heaths and downs of the countryside. This allowed plants to grow taller. New plants could grow because there were no rabbits to eat them. As a result, areas of the countryside changed forever. Different types of plants thrived and different animals attracted by these new plants moved in to feed on them.

27 Look back at the anchovetta food web. How would other organisms be affected if the numbers of anchovetta were reduced?

Poisoned food chains

It is not only energy that is transferred through a food chain. When animals eat plants they transfer chemicals to their bodies. Some of these chemicals may be harmful to the animals. In her book *The Silent Spring* (1963) Rachel Carson wrote of the dangers of the concentration of chemicals through a food chain.

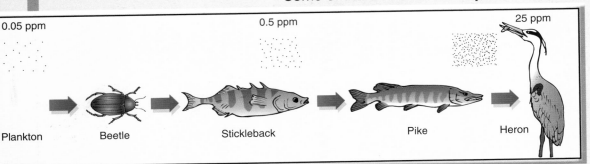

0.05 ppm   0.5 ppm   25 ppm

Plankton   Beetle   Stickleback   Pike   Heron

2.17 *The concentration of DDT increasing in the food chain*

2.18 *A bird poisoned by DDT*

DDT was first made in Germany in 1874. It was in the 1920s that the Swiss chemist Paul Muller showed that DDT could be used to kill insects such as mosquitoes, which spread diseases.

The first sprays worked well but in the 1940s the doses had to be increased because the insects seemed to be more difficult to kill. They were becoming resistant to the DDT. The dose was controlled so that it would not kill any of the birds and fish in the water where the insects bred.

In a lake, the water was covered with DDT. On the surface there was no apparent damage but plankton (small water plants and animals) were storing the DDT in their bodies. The concentration of DDT in the plankton was 250 times the dose sprayed from the air.

One fish can eat many thousands of plankton. The DDT was kept in the fishes' bodies. Although the quantity was not enough to kill the fish, it was concentrated in its fat. The concentration in the fish was found to be 12,000 times that in the plankton.

Birds ate the fish. They ate dozens of fish and the dose of poison from each fish was high so that soon the quantity of DDT in their body fat was enough to cause changes. The concentration of DDT in birds was found to be 80,000 times that found in fish.

The eggshells of the birds' eggs were thin. They broke each time a bird sat on its eggs to incubate them. This resulted in no new young so the birds' numbers rapidly fell.

Rachel Carson argued this change would affect the numbers of other animals and plants in the food chain.

28 Draw a food chain to illustrate this story.

29 Why does the DDT increase as it moves along the food chain?

30 What might happen to the numbers of fish if there were fewer birds?

Questions

1 The following is a food chain. Explain what it tells you.

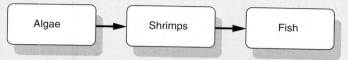

Algae → Shrimps → Fish

2 In the above food chain the algae is a type of plant. Why do all food chains start with plants?

3 Connect the sentences with the correct name.

a Organisms that eat animals.   Producers
b Organisms that can eat
both animals and plants.   Consumers
c Organisms that eat plants.   Carnivores
d Organisms that use other
organisms for their food.   Herbivores
e Organisms that make their own food.   Omnivores

4 The school grounds are part of the **biosphere**. The schools grounds are an **ecosystem** and scientists would study the **environment** of the **habitats** in it to learn about the relationships between the living **organisms**.

Write a sentence to describe what each of the words in bold mean to a scientist.

5 In a food chain where would we find the decomposers and why are they so important?

6 A food chain.

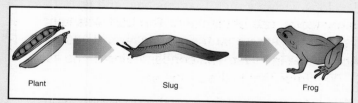

Plant   Slug   Frog

a Name a part of the frog that helps it move around its habitat.
b Describe two ways in which the frog has adapted to its environment.
c In the food chain which organism is the producer and which is the herbivore?

7 A food web in a wood.

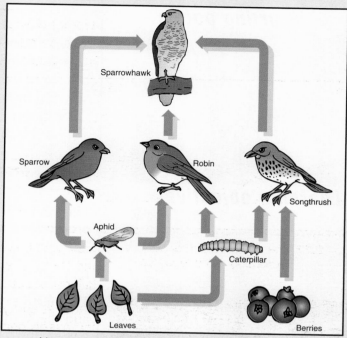

Sparrowhawk

Sparrow   Robin

Songthrush

Aphid

Caterpillar

Leaves   Berries

a Name one herbivore and one carnivore.
b The number of robins in the wood decrease. Why might the number of songthrushes or sparrows increase?
c How might that affect the number of sparrowhawks?
d What is the direction of energy flow in the wood?
e Which of the following diagrams describes the pyramid of numbers for the food chain?

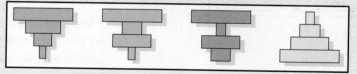

8 A food chain in a field.

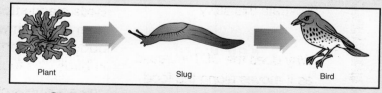

Plant   Slug   Bird

a Give one reason why the size of the organism gets bigger along the chain.
b Would the bird numbers decrease if the slugs were killed by poison? Give two reasons for your answer.

9 Explain why most of the energy produced by the plant does not end up in the bird.

UNIT 3 Reproduction

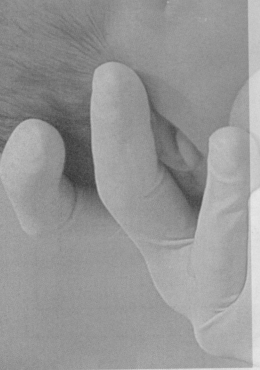

Starting points ▸

All living things carry out the same life processes. These include moving, growing, feeding, sensing, excreting waste, reproducing and getting energy from food by respiration. One of these, reproduction, is the process of producing a new organism.

The human animal has a life cycle that can be described as:

birth ⟶ infancy ⟶ childhood ⟶ adolescence ⟶ maturity ⟶ ageing ⟶ death

Learning objectives ▸

This unit will help you to know about and understand the ideas and processes involved in reproduction:

That animals have reproductive organs and different patterns of reproduction and development.

That fertilisation involves the fusion of the nuclei of sperm and egg and the fertilised egg divides into two, four, eight, etc. cells as it passes down the oviduct.

That sperm and egg cells are specially adapted for their functions and the nuclei contain the characteristics of male and female parents, respectively.

That egg cells are released from the ovaries at regular (approximately monthly) intervals and menstruation is a monthly cycle controlled by hormones, which stops during pregnancy.

That the foetus develops within a membranous bag, and is supported and cushioned by amniotic fluid. The placenta supplies nutrients and oxygen to the foetus via the umbilical cord and removes carbon dioxide and other waste products.

That harmful substances and viruses can cross the placenta into the foetus and affect development.

Key words ▸

amniotic fluid	follicle	nucleus	puberty
asexual reproduction	gamete	ova	seed
cervix	germination	ovary	sexual intercourse
ejaculation	gestation	ovulation	sexual reproduction
embryo	hormone	ovule	sperm
erection	implanted	ovum	testicles
fallopian tube	incubator	placenta	umbilical cord
fertilisation	labour	pollen grains	uterus
foetus	mature	pollination	
	menstruation	pregnant	

Learning summary ▼

This flow chart summarises the key learning points in this unit.

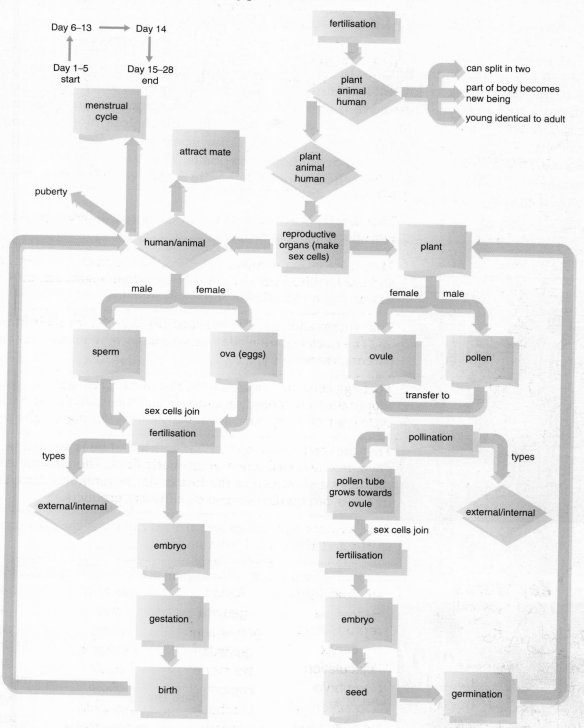

Use a flow chart of your own to make a summary of other units.

Reproduction in Humans

Galaxy Date 30000 pardecs

A Report to Planetary Life Research Department, Earth

The planet of Zamog in the Gestiliane System has a strange life form. They are green and stand in the light for up to 3 Zamog hours a day. They do not seem to eat but they drink a lot. Interestingly the atmosphere is a mixture of carbon dioxide and oxygen. They have a strange ritual in which they meet in a special area covered with soft material. They talk and after much laughter put their middle bodies together and wriggle around. Later some of the Zamogites go around the special site collecting oval-shaped deposits. These they put in special warm boxes. After 6 Zamog months a young Zamogite comes out of the box. This would appear to be the way Zamogs reproduce.

A fantasy story perhaps, but it poses some important questions about life and reproduction.

- What might life forms look like on another planet?

- How would we know they were alive?

- How would they increase in number or reproduce over time?

These are not such strange questions. All living things do the same things. Life is a set of processes that work when energy is transferred to them by a chemical reaction called respiration. These processes are easy to remember as MRS GREN:

Movement
Reproduction
Sensitivity or response to the environment
Growth
Respiration
Excretion
Nutrition

Our space creatures would share the same processes if they were alive. All life forms perform the entire set of above processes, all of which can be observed. So what can we see when we observe reproduction?

If our space life form is alive it will reproduce itself. This can be done in two ways.

- By splitting in two or growing a new life form from a small part of the body. This would be called asexual reproduction. Asexual reproduction involves cells splitting in two continually until a new adult is formed. The new individual is identical to the adult.

- By joining two special cells called sex cells together. This is called **sexual reproduction**.

Many animals and flowering plants reproduce by sexual reproduction. To do this they need **reproductive organs**. These organs produce special cells called **gametes** which each have some of the information needed to make a new individual. The male gamete contains half the information needed and the female contains the other half. It is contained in the nucleus of the gametes and is called **genetic information**.

To make a new individual by sexual reproduction the male gamete and female gamete must join together, or fuse. When this happens it is called **fertilisation**. After the male and female gametes have joined all the instructions to make a new individual are present.

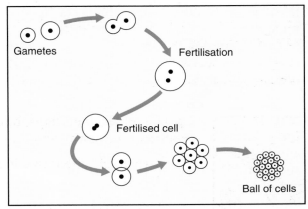

3.1 *Sexual reproduction by the fusion of two cells*

1. Describe the difference between sexual and asexual reproduction.

2. What are the special sex cells called?

3. Why is only half the information needed contained in one gamete?

After fertilisation the fertilised cell begins to divide into a ball of cells. This ball of cells develops into a new individual which is both similar to and different from its adult.

Fibonacci's reproducing numbers!

A man puts a pair of young rabbits in a field that is fully enclosed. The rabbits have all the food they need and do not die. At the end of the first month they are able to reproduce. They reproduce a new pair of rabbits each month. Nothing feeds on the rabbits and they are healthy so none die. How many pairs of rabbits will there be at the end of the year?

In 1202 Leonardo Fibonacci used this problem to illustrate a new number sequence.

He wrote a book, *Liber Abaci,* about this number problem, which became known as the Fibonacci series.

The answer is that at the end of the month the first rabbit pair will produce a new pair. Then at the end of the second month the two pairs produce a pair of rabbits, and at the end of the third month each pair produces a new pair, making three pairs. This would give the number sequence:

1,   1,   2,   3,   5,   8,   13,   21,   34,   55,   ∞

4. Work out the sequence and find the last two numbers in the series.

Sexual reproduction in flowering plants

3.2 *Cherry blossom*

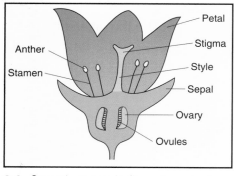

Petal
Anther
Stigma
Stamen
Style
Sepal
Ovary
Ovules

3.3 *Sexual organs in flowering plants*

5 How does a flower attract insects?

6 What are the differences between flowers designed to attract insects and those designed to be wind pollinated?

3.5 *Pollen tubes grown on a slide*

In many plants the flower is the centre for sexual reproduction. Inside the flower are found at least one set of sex organs, and usually two; one male and one female.

The cherry flower has both sets of sex organs. The anthers produce the male sex gamete carried in **pollen grains**, and the ovary produces the female sex gamete called the **ovule**. To make a new plant the male gamete has to fuse with the female gamete.

The problem flowers have is how to transfer the male gamete in the pollen to the female ovule. This is called **pollination**. They use insects or wind to transfer the male pollen.

Insect-pollinated flowers have sweet nectar that attracts insects. The nectar is a high-energy store and insects use it as a fuel. To make sure the insect takes the pollen, the nectar is positioned so that the insect must brush against the anthers in the male stamen to reach it. The pollen is hanging on the anther and is transferred to the insect's body. When the insect lands on another plant of the same species to take more nectar it will brush against the female stigma and leave pollen.

Wind pollination is a high-risk process. A lot of pollen is blown off the plant into the air and has to fall on the right plant and fertilise the female sex cells. To be successful the male anthers must grow out of the flower into the path of the blowing wind. The female stigma needs to grow outside the flower and be like a net to catch the pollen in the wind. This means the petals have to be small and on long stalks, like grass, or small and well spread out, like trees such as hazel or beech.

3.4 *Wind-pollinated grasses*

Once pollen has been transferred to the female part of a flower it still has to get to the female gamete. The pollen will grow a long tube from the stigma down the style to the ovule. A chemical made by the ovule guides the tube as it grows. The gametes travel from the pollen grains down the tube to the ovule where one male sex gamete joins with the female sex gamete, fertilising it.

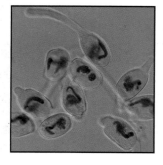

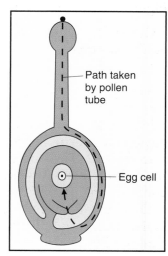

Path taken by pollen tube

Egg cell

3.6 *Fertilisation of an ovule by pollen*

Seeds are formed differently in different plants. Usually the fertilised cell divides and forms the **embryo**. Using food in the ovule it forms a food store and then toughens its outer walls. This is the **seed**. The seeds a plant makes are protected inside a fruit, made from the ovary. The fruits are shed from the plant and the seeds containing the embryo plants lie in the soil until conditions are right for them to **germinate**, or begin growing. A seed will often lie dormant and wait for the special conditions that will trigger germination and growth.

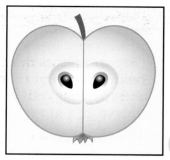

3.7 *Cross-section of an apple*

7 What are the differences between pollination, fertilisation and germination?

Sexual reproduction in animals

If our space life form reproduced sexually it would have special organs for producing sex cells. It would also need a special organ to transfer a sex cell to an adult of the opposite sex for fertilisation.

There are two things the space life form could then do to protect the developing individual. It could lay eggs that would hold the growing embryo, or an adult could hold on to the fertilised sex cells in a special part of its body where they would develop for a period of time called **gestation**.

During gestation the developing **embryo** needs to be fed and its waste removed. In an egg the waste is collected in a special part of the egg but in an animal the developing embryo needs to be nourished and have its waste removed inside the mother.

One of the most important features of sexual reproduction is the way animals attract a mate. Some animals do this with special courtship movements, which often involve males proving themselves by fighting other males. Other male animals attract females with their bright colouring. Flowers rely upon attracting insects and spreading their pollen to other plants. This means they need to have highly coloured or scented flowers.

Our space creature has courtship movements that are very easily observed!

Animal sex cells and fertilisation

In animals the gametes or sex cells are called **ova** (or eggs) and **sperm**. Sperm are the sex cells made by the male animal. They are very similar in all animals. They have all the parts a typical animal cell has but their nucleus contains only half of the set of instructions needed to make a new individual. They also have a **flagellum**, which is like a tiny tail and which beats to move the sperm through liquid.

3.8 *Single sperm cell*

3.9 *A single human ovum*

8 Why are birds' eggs larger than human eggs?

Ova, or egg cells, are the female gametes. They also have all of the parts of a typical animal cell. They do not have a flagellum and cannot move by themselves. Eggs vary in size from animal to animal. They are often very small, like the human egg cell, which is about 1 mm across. But they can be very large too, such as the eggs made by birds. The egg cells contain a store of food which is used by the embryo as it grows.

To make a new animal, sperm and ova must join together at fertilisation. A single sperm cell joins a single egg (**ovum**) and its nucleus is injected into the egg cell. The nuclei of the egg and sperm join together to make a new nucleus. The fertilised cell then has the full set of instructions needed to make a new individual.

3.10 *Fertilisation of ovum by sperm*

Patterns of reproduction

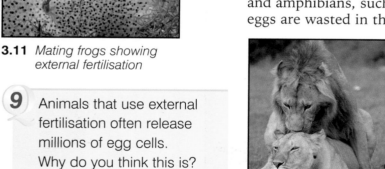

3.11 *Mating frogs showing external fertilisation*

9 Animals that use external fertilisation often release millions of egg cells. Why do you think this is?

10 Look at a chicken's egg. Why do you think it is the shape it is?

11 What are the advantages and disadvantages of laying eggs?

Animals have many different ways of making fertilisation happen. In some, the eggs are fertilised by sperm outside the parents' body. This is called **external fertilisation**, and is common in animals that live in water. The parents simply release their sex cells into the water of the sea, lake or pond in which they live. The sperm swim through the water and if they find an egg, fuse with it to make a fertilised cell. Fish and amphibians, such as frogs and toads, reproduce in this way. Many eggs are wasted in this process because sperm do not find them.

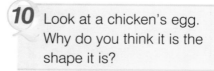

3.12 *Mating mammals*

In other animals such as birds and mammals, the ovum is fertilised inside the female's body. Male animals introduce their sperm into the female's reproductive organs. When this happens it is called **internal fertilisation**. This increases the chances of sperm and eggs coming together, so the females need to make only a small number of eggs. In many animals only one egg cell is ready for fertilisation at a time.

Eggs that are fertilised inside the female's body can be looked after more easily. Reptiles' and birds' eggs provide a large food store. The egg is passed outside the body but is protected by a shell as the new individual grows.

In most mammals, including humans, the new individual grows inside the body of the mother and gets its food from her blood.

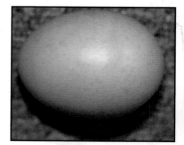

3.13 *Chicken's egg*

Sexual reproduction in humans

Male reproductive organs

Humans are mammals and generally all mammals reproduce in the same way. The male produces gametes called **sperm** in his **testicles**. There are generally two testicles contained in a bag called a **scrotum**. The testicles connect to the **penis** by a tube called a **sperm tube**.

The human male will only start to produce sperm after puberty. During puberty the male sex hormone testosterone starts to be produced and causes changes in boys. The voice becomes deeper, face and body hair appears, and the sex organs grow bigger.

After puberty a healthy mature male makes hundreds of millions of sperm each day but they take two months to mature and start moving. The sperm are well designed for their job, streamlined with a bullet-shaped head and a long whip-like tail. The head carries half the genetic messages needed to make a new individual.

Wrapped around the top of the sperm's tail just behind the head are special structures for transferring energy very quickly. The testicles also make a sugar-containing liquid called **semen**. This liquid provides the sperm with the chemical energy they need to move.

The first human to see a sperm cell was Leeuwenhoek. He saw the head as a blob and thought it must contain a tiny human.

12 In male mammals the sex organs hang outside the body. Why do you think that is?

13 What advantages does this have for the animals?

14 Why would the energy-producing part be behind the head and in front of the tail of the sperm?

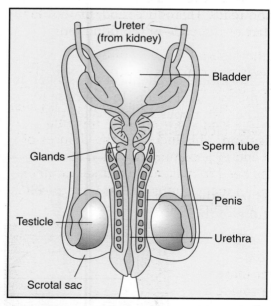

3.14 *Male reproductive organs*

Ureter (from kidney)
Bladder
Glands
Sperm tube
Testicle
Penis
Urethra
Scrotal sac

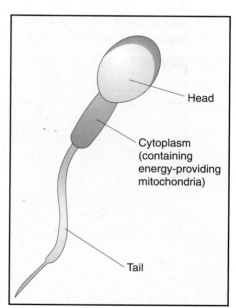

3.15 *A sperm cell*

Head
Cytoplasm (containing energy-providing mitochondria)
Tail

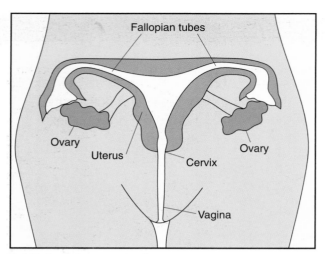

3.16 *Female reproductive organs*

Female reproductive organs

Human females are born with millions of immature eggs in two **ovaries**. These are all the eggs a female will ever need. They are contained in small sacs or **follicles** in the ovaries. They lie dormant until the female enters puberty. During puberty, female sex hormones like oestrogen are produced and changes occur in girls. Their breasts develop, body hair appears and periods start.

After puberty one egg develops each month. The follicle containing it gets bigger and feeds the egg until it is ready to be released into the fallopian tube and pass down to the uterus. The uterus is where a baby develops inside the female's body. It has great elasticity. Its normal length is about 7.5 cm and it can stretch to 30 cm to hold a developing baby. The cervix is the opening between the uterus and the vagina.

15 Why do the eggs have to be fertilised inside the mother?

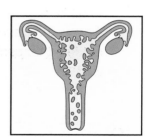

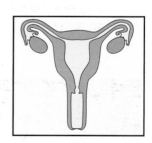

The menstrual cycle

Days 1 to 5

From puberty a woman releases one egg a month from the ovaries. She will continue to do this until about the age of 50 when the production of eggs ceases. If the ovum is not fertilised it will pass out of the woman's body. Sex hormone levels drop. This causes the wall of the uterus to break down. Blood and dead cells including the unfertilised ovum pass out of the vagina. This is a period, or **menstruation**, and marks the start of the cycle of reproduction.

Days 6 to 13

A gland in the brain produces a **hormone**, or chemical messenger. It tells the ovary to prepare for the release of an ovum. In response to the hormone the ovary secretes other hormones which makes the uterus lining grow thick and fill with blood. It is ready to nourish a baby if the ovum is fertilised.

Day 14

On day 14 the ovum is released from the ovary and passes down the **fallopian tube** to the **uterus**. This is called **ovulation**.

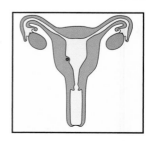

16 What is the length of the menstrual cycle?

17 Why do mammals have a menstrual cycle?

Days 15 to 28

If a sperm has entered the fallopian tube it may fuse with the ovum and fertilise it. The fertilised ovum will sink into the thick wall of the uterus. Here it will develop into an embryo. During this time the sex hormone level remains high so the fertilised ovum stays in the woman's body.

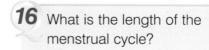

Start of a new individual

Before **sexual intercourse** can take place the sexual organs have to be prepared. The male and female touching causes the male's penis to fill with blood and stand up so that it becomes erect. This **erection** makes it possible to slide the penis into the female's vagina. During the touching the vagina swells, and becomes moist and slippery. This makes it easier for the penis to enter the vagina.

The moving of the penis backwards and forwards in the vagina stimulates the release of sperm into the female. The release is a pumping of sperm and semen and is called an **ejaculation**.

Ejaculation pushes millions of sperm and semen deep into the vagina and muscular movements in the female help them to enter the fallopian tube. If sexual intercourse takes place during ovulation, it is here the two sex gametes can meet and fuse. Normally only one sperm will fertilise the ovum. The head of the sperm forces its way into the ovum leaving its tail on the outside. The wall of the ovum immediately becomes harder to penetrate so that other sperms cannot enter the ovum.

The ovum divides again and again forming a ball of cells that sink down into the wall of the uterus. The ball of cells divides and starts to form special tissue cells which will develop into organs. The developing **embryo** is **implanted** in the uterus so it can continue to grow. The female is now **pregnant**. Growth is the continuous dividing of cells to form new tissues and organs in the developing baby.

During the next 10 weeks, the embryo grows rapidly. Its cells keep on dividing and making new cells, and it begins to look like a small human being. The embryo is now called a **foetus**. A network of blood vessels called the **placenta** form in the uterus. Joining the placenta and the foetus is the **umbilical cord**. It is through the placenta that the mother supplies the developing foetus with oxygen, water and food. They pass from the mother's blood supply into the blood of the foetus. Harmful substances like drugs, alcohol or nicotine can also pass through the placenta into the baby's blood. It is important for pregnant women to avoid these substances.

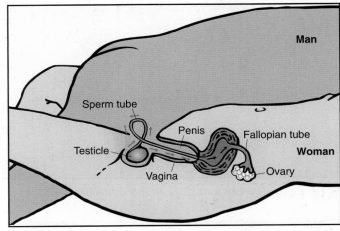

3.17 *Human sexual intercourse*

18 What is the advantage of ejaculation rather than just putting the sperm into the female?

19 Why is it important that only one sperm can fertilise an egg?

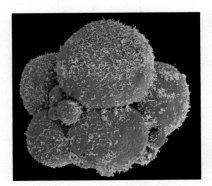

3.18 *This ball of cells is the start of a new life*

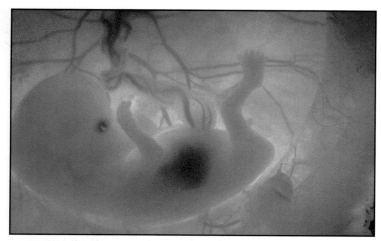

3.19 *An 8–10 week foetus. Note the umbilical cord*

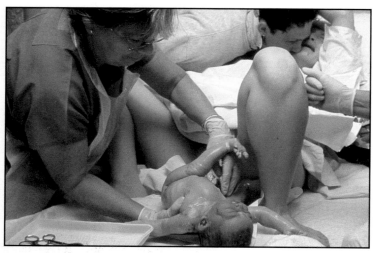

3.20 *Giving birth*

The placenta also carries away waste such as carbon dioxide. Over the next few months the embryo develops into a new organism. This period is called **gestation** and in a human lasts for 9 months. Throughout this time the baby is protected by a watery liquid in the uterus called **amniotic fluid**.

After 9 months the baby is ready to be born. Normally the baby will have moved so that its head is at the bottom of the uterus so that it can be born head first. The amniotic fluid leaks out and the female feels powerful muscular contractions in the uterus. This is called **labour**. The contractions cause the **cervix,** the narrow opening to the uterus, to widen and allow the baby to pass out through the vagina. After birth the umbilical cord is cut and sealed off. The short piece left attached to the baby will form the umbilicus, or belly button. Meanwhile the female expels the placenta through her vagina.

Human babies are born after a gestation of 9 months and weigh about 3–4 kilograms. In the animal kingdom gestation periods differ. One of the smallest mammal babies is the opossum, which is born after a gestation of 13 days and is the size of a wheat grain. One of the largest mammal babies on land is the elephant, which has a gestation period of 20 months, while the blue whale has the biggest baby of all, after a gestation period of 11 months, with a weight of 2 tonnes.

20 Why do you think the length of gestation is different in different animals?

21 What do you think is the advantage of a big birth weight?

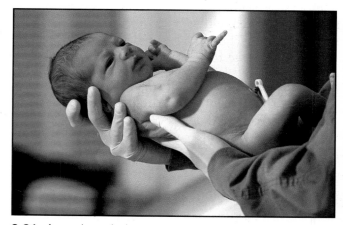

3.21 *A newborn baby*

Find out more about human development at ▶ **www.scienceweb.co.uk**

Growing up

As a child grows, cells carry on dividing throughout its body. Each cell makes two new ones when it divides and each new cell grows bigger until it divides again. As a result, a child grows steadily larger and heavier. However, not all of the body's parts grow at the same rate. Cell division happens more quickly in some places than others. The arms and legs grow much more quickly than the head, for example. The head is almost fully grown at birth and grows very little after that.

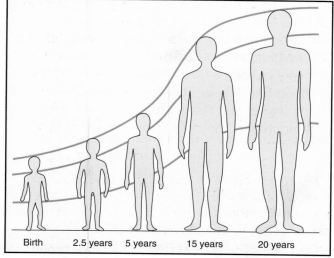

3.22 *Human growth curves. Note the growth spurt at puberty*

Eventually we all stop growing, but our cells do not stop dividing. They just slow down a bit. In an adult, new cells are only made to replace cells which die or are damaged in some way.

The period of fastest growth in your body happens during **puberty**, some time between the ages of 9 and 15 (the exact timing varies from one person to another). This is also the time when your body becomes sexually **mature**, when boys start producing sperm and girls start menstruating. The changes which take place at this time mean that your body is able to reproduce – make children. Some of the changes are easy to see, but others are less obvious. For example, the shape of a boy's voice box changes and his voice becomes deeper.

The changes that happen during puberty are switched on and controlled by chemicals called hormones which are made in different parts of the body, including the brain, the testicles and the ovaries. These chemicals pass into the blood and travel all over the body. They control how quickly some cells divide and what they do. In a girl hormones cause the ovaries to start ripening eggs, and to release one each month as the menstrual cycle continues. In boys different hormones cause the testicles to start making sperm cells.

Although puberty is the age at which your body can begin to reproduce, humans do not normally start making babies for several more years. Before you are ready to take on the responsibility of making and looking after a baby, there is a lot more growing up to do.

22 Between which ages is the child growing fastest?

23 What do you think the upper and lower lines on the graph represent?

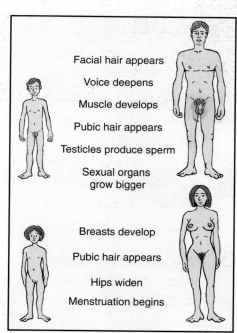

Facial hair appears
Voice deepens
Muscle develops
Pubic hair appears
Testicles produce sperm
Sexual organs grow bigger

Breasts develop
Pubic hair appears
Hips widen
Menstruation begins

3.23 *Changes during puberty*

24 What changes happen to boys' and girls' bodies during puberty?

TECHNOLOGY BOX

Special treatment

Some newborn babies need special care in hospital. This is most often because they are premature, which means they have been born early, or because they are very small. These babies are often looked after in a special unit in the hospital. They are very tiny and some of their organs may not yet be working properly. They may be cared for in an **incubator**.

Amy had only grown inside her mother's uterus for 28 weeks when she was born. She weighed only 1.85 kg. Her body is so small that she loses heat very quickly. She cannot suck yet and so her mother cannot breastfeed her. The incubator provides care for her rather like her mother's uterus did. There are many wires and machines attached to the incubator. They look a bit scary, but they are very important.

Amy's incubator is warmed by a heater. She needs to be kept warm so that her body can develop normally. Her body temperature is monitored by sensors and the heater is controlled by a computer. If she gets too warm, the heater is turned down.

Amy needs food to provide energy and materials to help her grow. Since she cannot suck she is fed by a tube passing through her nose and going straight into her stomach. A special milky food mixture is passed through this tube to fed her. Over the next couple of weeks, she will grow and get stronger using the nutrients in this food. Eventually she will be able to feed on her mother's milk.

3.24 *A premature baby in an incubator*

25 Why are premature babies so small?

26 How was Amy kept warm in her mother's uterus?

27 How did Amy get nutrients when she was in the uterus?

28 Why is contact between Amy and her mother so important?

The nurses who work in this unit are specially trained. They know how to make sure that Amy is looked after as well as if she were still growing in the uterus. They use the monitors and computers to control the environment in the incubator, in the same way the environment in the uterus was controlled by her mother's body.

Amy's mother visits her several times a day. It is important for her to have lots of contact with Amy. She can stroke and cuddle Amy by putting her hands through the holes in the sides of the incubator. As soon as Amy is strong enough to feed normally, she will leave the incubator and be cared for at home by her mother.

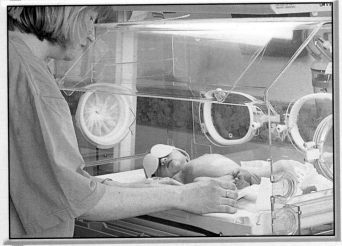

3.25 *Amy's mother can stroke her while she is in the incubator*

Questions

1 The diagram below shows a baby developing inside its mother.

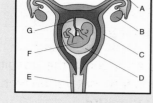

a Name the organ system shown and the parts labelled A–G.

b In which part of the organ system are the eggs produced?

c Through which part does food get to the baby?

d This part also transfers another important chemical to the baby. What is that chemical?

2 The diagram below shows the human menstrual cycle.

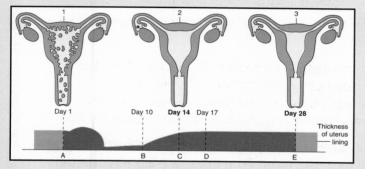

a Describe what is happening at each of the following stages.

  i In 1 the lining...............

  ii At A on day 1...............

  iii In 2 the lining...............

  iv At B on day 10...............

  v At C on day 14...............

  vi At D on day 17...............

  vii In 3 the lining...............

  viii At E on day 28...............

b The uterus needs a thick lining for...............

c If the egg is fertilised it...............

3 The diagram on the right shows a part of the human male.

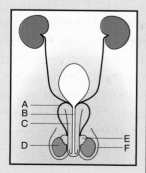

a Name the organ system and label the parts.

b In which part are the sperm cells produced?

c The diagram is of a sperm cell.

  i Why does it have a long tail?

  ii What is contained inside the large head?

  iii What is the purpose of the collar behind the head?

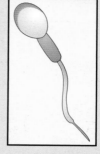

4 Sex cells are called ....

5 When an organism produces two different cells that join together to make a new individual, it is called .... reproduction.

6 Complete the following passage by filling in the missing words.

The sex organs make up the............... The female produces egg cells or ....in the............... The egg is released and passes into the............... The egg cell will stay in the uterus only if it is fertilised. Sexual intercourse happens when the male inserts his...............into the female's...............and releases sperm. The sperm can travel along the............... to join or...............with the egg cell or............... This is called fertilisation. If the egg is not fertilised the wall of the uterus and egg cells are broken down and passed out of the............... This is called...............

7 Give one reason why sexual reproduction makes each new individual unique.

8 Complete the following passage by filling in the missing words.

When young humans reach a certain period between 10 and 18 years they undergo changes. This age is called............... During this time, ... start to make sperm in............... Females start to produce sex hormones and start............... every 28 days. Other changes happen, like............... of the voice in boys and growth of .... hair in both boys and girls.

9 The period of time a foetus develops in the uterus is called...............

10 Give one reason why a big birth weight would be an advantage in mammals.

UNIT 4 Variation

There are many different types of living thing and they differ from each other in many ways. Each type is called a species. All living things can be put into groups whose members have certain things in common. The two main groups of living things are plants and animals.

To identify and sort living things we need to look at their features. Usually we compare what their bodies are like. When you need to find the name of an animal or plant you can look for a picture of it or you could use a 'key'. A 'key' is like a branching diagram or a series of questions which helps us check the features of our specimen and follow clues which help to identify it.

Learning objectives ▶

This unit will help you learn about and understand the ideas and processes to do with the differences between living things:

What scientists mean by a 'species'.

That members of the same species have many similarities but also many differences and that these differences are called variations.

About how we measure and record variations.

About some variations that occur in humans and in other living things.

That some variations are caused by environmental differences.

That some variations are inherited from parents.

About why scientists classify living things into groups.

That living things belonging to the same group have things in common and are different from other groups.

About the features which some groups of living things have in common.

Key words ▶

binomial system	correlation	inherit	positive correlation
classification	discontinuous variation	invertebrate	species
continuous variation	environment	kingdom	variation
	genus	negative correlation	vertebrate

Learning summary ▽

This mind map summarises the key learning points in this unit.

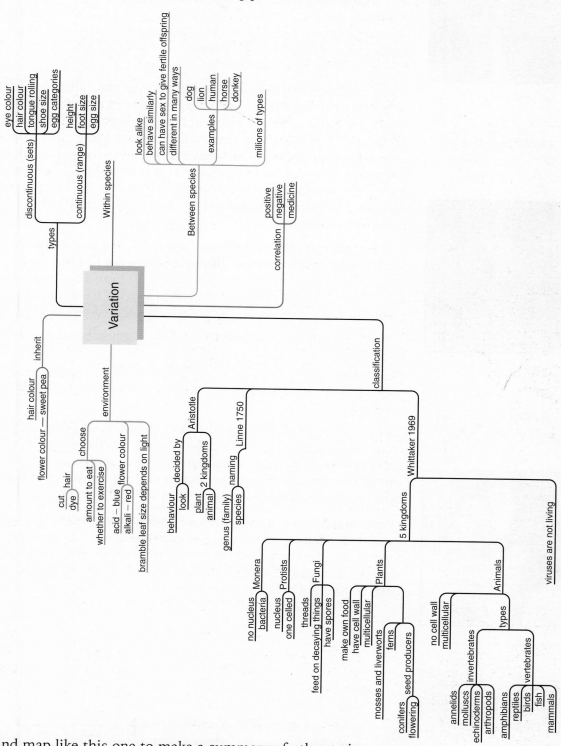

Use a mind map like this one to make a summary of other units.

A new species

4.1 *Explorers in the rainforest*

1 Why is the rainforest being destroyed?

4.2 *A mule*

2 Is a mule a species? Explain your answer.

4.3 *'Bigfoot'*

3 What evidence would you need before you accept that a new species has been discovered?

Deep in the rainforests of Brazil, the team of explorers from 'Biolink' are hard at work. They have spent the last 6 months moving deeper and deeper into the forest, examining each plant and animal they find closely, and identifying them using keys and reference books. Each week or so the native people of the forest take the explorers to a new site. The explorers are keen to go because the natives know of plants and animals which the scientists have never seen before.

The explorers are not in the rainforest for fun. They work for a company that specialises in finding new types of living thing. There are more different kinds of living things found in the rainforest than anywhere else on Earth. Each week new types of living thing are found, which have never been seen or studied by scientists. Some of these discoveries are very important. Many are known to provide cures for diseases in humans. It is important to discover these living things before their environment, the rainforest, is destroyed.

There are millions of different types of living things on Earth. Each distinct type is called a **species**. Members of the same species have features in common. They all look alike and behave in similar ways. Members of the same species have more in common with each other than with any other living thing.

Usually, sexual reproduction can only happen between two individuals which are members of the same species. For example humans can only make babies with other humans, dogs with other dogs, salmon with other salmon and garden peas with other garden peas.

There are rare exceptions to this rule, however. For example, a horse and a donkey are two different species. But they can mate and produce an animal called a mule. Their reproduction is not totally successful, though, because a mule is always sterile and it cannot reproduce at all.

Sometimes the discovery of a so-called new species hits the headlines. Many explorers in the Himalayas are on the look-out for the yeti, an animal which is said to be both like a bear and a man. In America a similar animal called 'Bigfoot' is alleged to have been filmed but many people believe that the film was a fake.

Find out more about discovering new living things on the Internet at
▶ **www.scienceweb.co.uk**

Differences between individuals

Although all members of a species have much in common, they can be different in many ways. For example, all the humans you know belong to the same species, but they are all different from each other – otherwise you would not be able to tell one person from another!

The differences between individuals are called **variations**. All dogs belong to the same species too, but the dogs in the picture are different in many ways.

4.4 All sorts of dog

4 List the differences between the dogs in the picture. These differences are variations.

Measuring variations

Jane carried out a survey of the variation in her class at school. She collected data about each pupil.

Some variations are easy to measure and record as a graph. Eyes are either blue, green or brown. People either can or cannot roll their tongue into a U-shape. Hair comes in definite colours, and may be blond, black, brown or red. Differences like this are called **discontinuous variation**. Individuals can be put in one set or another depending on what characteristics they have.

Other variations are not so easy to record. When Jane measured the heights of pupils in her class, most of the measurements were different. She could not easily draw a bar chart from this data. It seemed that her friends could be any height between 120 and 169 cm. Differences like this are called **continuous variation**. The characteristic can be any measurement within a **range**.

Jane's friend Anna suggested that they should add some bits of data together by putting them into different size classes. They made up their own size classes, going up in 10 cm steps. They could draw a graph using these classes.

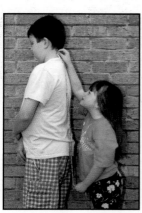

4.5 Girl measuring height of a boy

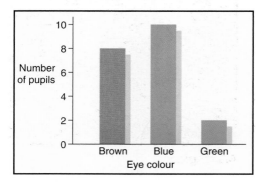

4.6 Bar chart of eye colours in pupils

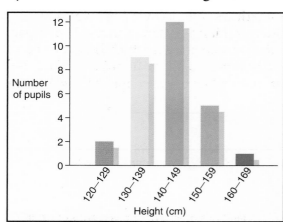

4.7 Bar chart showing variations in children's height

5 What other human characteristics show continuous variation?

The sizes of humans and of different parts of their bodies show continuous variation. Clothes and shoe manufacturers know about this and take it into account when they mass-produce clothes in different sizes. They cannot make items to fit each individual's personal measurements. This would take too long. Instead they group people with similar sizes together into different size classes and make only a limited range of sizes.

So people who wear size 6 shoes actually have feet which may be different sizes when measured in millimetres. And trousers which have a 65 cm waist probably fit people with waist measurements ranging from 62 to 68 cm.

Looking for links

As they looked at their data Jane and Anna began to notice patterns.

"Blond haired pupils all have blue eyes," said Jane.

"Yes," said Anna, "and taller children have a bigger chest measurement."

"I'm not so sure about that," Jane replied. "Look at John's data. He is tall but his chest measurement is as small as David's."

When two characteristics seem to be linked in some way we say there is a **correlation** between them. This might happen when people who have a high value for one characteristic, such as height, also tend to have a high value for the other, such as chest size. Examples like this are called **positive correlations**.

6 Do you think there is a link between height and chest measurement? How could you be sure?

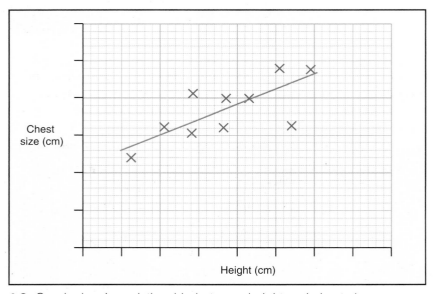

4.8 *Graph showing relationship between height and chest size*

Sometimes a correlation happens the other way around. Individuals who have a high value for one characteristic tend to have a *low* value for the other. An example of this would be that people who exercise a lot tend to have a lower resting pulse rate. Where this happens it is called a **negative correlation**.

On a school trip to the seaside Jane and Anna walked around the rocks, looking at the different animals and plants which lived there.

They noticed the limpets living on the rocks. Limpets have shells covering their soft bodies. There were many different sizes of limpet on the shore. Some had taller shells than others.

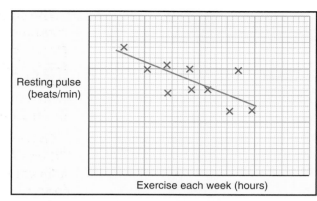

4.9 *Graph showing negative correlation*

Jane thought that the limpets with the tall shells also had the widest shells. Anna didn't agree. "I think that the height and width of the shells have nothing to do with each other," she said. "A limpet with a tall shell could just as easily have a wide or a narrow shell."

Size of limpet shells	
Height (mm)	Width (mm)
46	33
40	22
31	14
40	22
40	23
39	25
48	25
36	13
28	10
30	15
25	10
29	13
52	30
39	20
40	21
47	25
45	21
33	22
34	20
31	13

4.10 *Limpet measurements*

To find out who was right, they measured the height and width of 20 limpet shells and took their data back to school to plot graphs.

7 Draw a graph of the limpet data to find whether there is a correlation between height and width of shells.

8 What does your graph tell you? Explain what the results show.

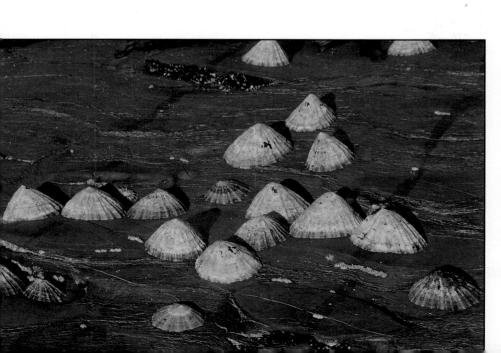

4.11 *Limpets on a rocky shore*

TECHNOLOGY BOX

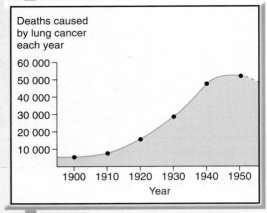

4.12 *Increase in lung cancer deaths 1900–1950*

9 Why had the amounts of these substances in the environment gone up since the start of the 20th century?

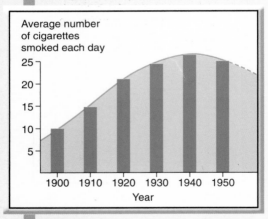

4.13 *Increase in average number of cigarettes smoked 1900–1950*

10 Describe the pattern shown in each of the two graphs.

11 Explain why the data suggests there is a link between smoking cigarettes and lung cancer deaths.

Medical correlation

Investigating correlation is an important part of medical science. Doctors often have to look for links between different things to find out what causes a disease.

At the start of the last century very few people died from lung cancer in Britain. Then in the 1940s and 1950s there was an alarming increase in the number of deaths from lung cancer. The government called in a team of scientists and doctors to investigate the cause of this increase. They knew that lung cancer was caused by poisonous substances in the environment. They needed to find which chemical was linked with the increase in the disease.

The doctors made a list of substances which might be harmful. They needed to find one which had been used increasingly since the start of the century. Their list included several suspects:

* road tar   * air pollution   * cigarette smoke

To begin with they thought the most likely cause of the increase in lung cancer was road tar. This contained some really nasty chemicals known to be toxic. Many doctors at that time did not consider that smoking cigarettes was harmful at all.

The team looked for a correlation between the lung cancer deaths and the presence of each substance. They were soon able to rule out road tar. Although many roads were covered with it, the chemical did not find its way into the air easily. It soon became apparent that only one factor was closely linked to lung cancer and that factor was smoking cigarettes.

Cigarette smoking was not particularly popular in Britain until the Great War of 1914–18. During that war, many of the soldiers began to smoke cigarettes which they were given freely. When they returned from the war they continued to smoke, and the fashion became more and more popular.

To confirm their suspicions, the research team carried out an investigation into the smoking habits of people who had lung cancer, and found a definite link. The more cigarettes a person smoked the greater was the chance of their developing lung cancer. Although some non-smokers developed cancer, it was much more common in smokers.

12 What would you expect to happen to the numbers dying from lung cancer? Give reasons for your answer.

Causes of variation

What you look like depends on two things.

You **inherit** some features from your parents. Their eggs and sperm contain genetic instructions which determine how you will grow and how you will look. Members of a family often look similar to each other. They have features in common which have been passed on in the instructions in the parents' eggs and sperm. We cannot change features which are easily inherited.

Some of your features are caused by things you do or the **environment** you live in. You may choose to dye your hair, grow it long, or cut it short. You may eat more or less food than a brother or sister, and so weigh more or less. You may play a lot of active sports and develop larger muscles than a friend who stays in and reads more.

No two human beings are exactly the same. Even identical twins, who have the same genetic instructions from their parents, are different in some ways. We all make choices about how we look and what we do and our environment has an effect on how we look.

The same is true for all living things. The cattle in the picture all belong to the same species, but are different in some ways.

4.15 *Mixed herd of cattle*

The colours of flowers in plants are often inherited. In dandelions, for example, the yellow flower colour is an inherited feature. In some plants, however, flower colour is affected by the environment. This is true of hydrangeas. They have red flowers if they grow in alkaline soils and blue flowers in acidic soils.

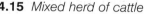
4.14 *Mother and daughter*

13 What features has this girl inherited from her mother?

14 Make a list of some of the features which are caused by differences in choice or environment.

15 What inherited variations can you observe in these cattle?

16 Which of these plants is growing in acid soil and which in alkaline soil?

17 How could you show that the colour difference in hydrangeas is not inherited?

4.16 *Red and blue hydrangeas*

HISTORY BOX
Scientific classification

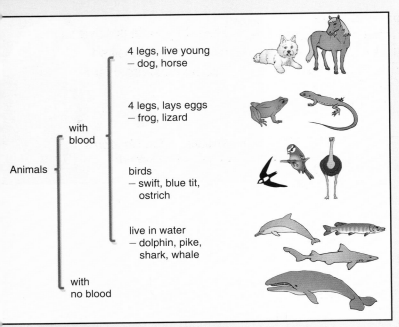

4 legs, live young
– dog, horse

4 legs, lays eggs
– frog, lizard

birds
– swift, blue tit,
ostrich

live in water
– dolphin, pike,
shark, whale

with
blood

Animals

with
no blood

4.17 *Part of Aristotle's classification*

T o be useful information needs to be organised. Scientists have always had problems organising the information they collect about living things.

The ancient Greek scientist Aristotle realised that he needed to organise all the living things he knew to help his studies. He made careful observations of various species and used these observations to sort them into groups. He sorted all living things into two **kingdoms** – animals and plants. He then put animals with similar features into smaller groups and described the species within each group. This is called **classification**.

Aristotle's system was hierarchical, with several layers of organisation. The features he used to sort the groups were often to do with how the animals behaved or where they lived. Because of this he put different animals together in the same group. For example, whales were grouped with fish because they lived in water, and any small animal which had lots of legs was classified as an insect.

This system worked quite well for hundreds of years. But during the 17th century explorers discovered more and more living things from all over the world and soon Aristotle's system would no longer do.

Carolus Linnaeus spent his life working on this problem. He wanted to find a better way to classify all known species. By 1750 he had developed a system of classification where the species was the smallest unit. He grouped the species into higher and higher categories. To do this he had to:

● look more closely at the bodies of living things and use their features to put them into groups;

● invent a new system for naming living things.

Names were causing confusion for scientists. The same species had different names in different countries, or even in different parts of the same country. A new system could help scientists working in different languages to communicate their ideas more easily. Linnaeus decided to use Latin to name the species.

Each species was given a name made from two words. The first word tells what type of animal it is (the **genus** or family name); the second tells the species of animal. This is called the **binomial** system. For example, the common buttercup found on lawns is called *Ranunculus repens*. The family name *Ranunculus* is the name for all buttercup-like plants. The species name *repens* means 'creeping' in Latin. So the buttercup in your garden is the 'creeping buttercup'.

18 Why do scientists need to classify living things?

19 What was wrong with putting whales and fish in the same group?

20 What does binomial mean?

Classification of living things

Since Linnaeus invented his classification system more and more living things have been discovered. Many of these are microscopic, and not like animals and plants at all. In 1969 Robert Whittaker came up with a new way of grouping living things which helped to solve some of these problems. He devised the 'five kingdoms' system. The new kingdoms he described made it possible to sort out some of the problem organisms.

Monera
Microscopic organisms whose cells have no nucleus. They include bacteria.

Protists
Organisms which have only one cell. Each cell has a nucleus inside it.

Fungi
Made of many thin, thread-like cells called hyphae. They feed on decaying matter. They reproduce by making spores. Many are microscopic but some can grow quite large.

Plants
Make their own food using light energy from the Sun. They have a pigment called chlorophyll that absorbs the light. They have a tough cell wall around each cell. Most are multicellular.

Animals
Need to eat other organisms to get their food. They are made of cells with a permeable wall around them. Most are multicellular.

The virus – living or not?

Viruses are very strange things. They are microscopic – even smaller than bacteria. Each virus is made of a 'body' which is a tough shell of protein. Some have special attachments to this body which help them break into living cells in other organisms. Inside the shell there is no cell membrane and no cytoplasm; the virus is not made of cells like other living things. What is inside is a single strand of the material that carries the information needed to make more viruses. It is called viral DNA.

Viruses do not feed at all. They cannot reproduce by themselves either. All they do is to break into cells in other living things and take them over for a while. They cause the nucleus of the cell to make millions more viruses, which then burst out of the cell and look for others to invade. Unfortunately, when they attack our cells they cause illnesses like measles and flu.

21 How do you think Aristotle would have classified microscopic organisms?

4.18 *Whittaker's 'five kingdoms' classification system*

22 Fungi used to be classified as plants but not any more. What are the differences between fungi and plants?

23 Why do you think some scientists do not classify a virus as a living thing at all?

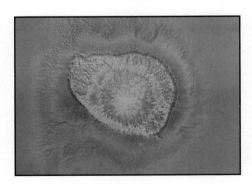

4.19 *A virus*

Classification of the plant kingdom

The living things in each of the five kingdoms are sorted into other groups. Each of these groups contains many species, which all have things in common.

The main plant groups

Mosses and liverworts
These simple plants have very thin leaves. They have no proper roots or stems and can only live in very wet places. They reproduce by making spores.

Ferns
These plants have strong stems, roots and leaves. They can live in drier places on land. They reproduce by making spores.

Seed producers
This is the largest group of plants. They have strong roots and stems and can control the loss of water from their leaves. They have developed many special adaptations and live in water and on land – even in desert regions. They all reproduce by making seeds.

There are many species of seed-producing plants. They are divided into two large groups:

- **conifers**
  Conifers are usually trees with woody stems. They have needle-like leaves that can stay on the tree for several years. They make seeds inside cones, which are their reproductive organs.

- **flowering plants**
  There are more species of flowering plants than any other group. They all make seeds in flowers, which contain their reproductive organs.

24 What does 'adaptation' mean?

25 What do **all** plants have in common?

26 Why do you think there are more species of flowering plant than any other group?

27 Find the names of the plants pictured on this page.

Classification of the animal kingdom

Like plants the animal kingdom is classified into many groups. The species in each group have a lot in common, but are very different from other groups.

The main animal groups

Annelids
These have long tube-shaped bodies made up of segments. Many burrow in soil or sand. They have bristles on their segments which help them burrow.

Molluscs
Molluscs' bodies are soft and not divided into segments. They move around using a muscular foot. Most have a hard shell for protection.

Arthropods
These have bodies divided into segments. They have jointed legs. They have a hard skeleton outside their bodies and antennae or feelers on their heads.

Echinoderms
These all live in the sea and have a tough spiny skin. Their bodies have a pattern made of five parts. They move around on tube feet.

Chordates
These all have a skeleton made of bone or cartilage inside their bodies. They have a front and rear end, with a brain at the front, and a spinal cord nerve. The chordates, more commonly called **vertebrates,** are divided into five main groups.

28 Which of the groups above do you think slugs belong to? Give reasons for your answer.

29 Which of the groups above do you think woodlice belong to? Give reasons for your answer.

30 The annelids, molluscs, echinoderms and arthropods are often grouped together and called **invertebrates**. Why do you think this is?

Find out more about the groups of living things on the Internet at
▶ **www.scienceweb.co.uk**

The vertebrates

Fish
These live in water all the time and have a scaly skin. They breathe through gills.

Amphibians
These have a smooth moist skin. The adults breathe on land through lungs but their young have gills. They mate in water and fertilisation takes place outside the body. The female lays eggs with jelly, which hatch into tadpoles.

Reptiles
These have a dry scaly skin and breathe through lungs. When they mate fertilisation takes place inside the female's body. She lays eggs with a tough leathery shell.

Birds
These all have feathers and wings and most can fly. They have beaks but no teeth. When they mate fertilisation takes place inside the female's body. She lays eggs with a hard shell. They can control their own temperature.

Mammals
These have hair or fur covering their skin, and breathe through lungs. When they mate fertilisation takes place inside the female's body. The young are well developed when they are born. The female cares for the young and feeds them on milk made in mammary glands.

31 Why is a snake a reptile and not a fish?

32 Although whales and dolphins live in water they belong to the mammal group. Why is this?

A strange animal

The duck-billed platypus is a strange animal found only in Australia. It has a bill which looks like that of a duck, and it reproduces by laying eggs, like reptiles and birds do. Its body is covered with fur.

4.20 *Duck-billed platypus*

33 Which group of animals does the duck-billed platypus belong to? Give reasons for your answer.

Questions

1 A class collected some data about variation in their year group in the school. There are two sets of data presented below.

Data set A			
Features	**Variation**	**No.**	**%**
Eye colour	Brown	36	28
	Blue	48	38
	Green	20	15
	Hazel	24	19
Hair colour	Blond	32	25
	Brown	51	40
	Black	35	27
	Red	10	8
Height	135–144	13	10
	145–154	64	50
	155–164	47	37
	165–174	4	3

Data set B			
Features	**Variation**	**No.**	**%**
Foot size	Small	23	18
	Medium	84	66
	Large	21	16
Hand size	Small	21	16
	Medium	90	70
	Large	17	14
Scars on	Hands	13	10
	Legs	86	67
	None	29	23

a Which of the above sets of data would be called discontinuous variables?

b Give a reason why.

c What would the other set of data be called and why?

d Give a pair of features that would show some positive correlation with each other.

e Explain why they have a positive correlation.

f Which features could be inherited and which could be environmental?

2 Use the following data to draw two pie charts of the distribution of the features.

Features	**Variation**	**No.**	**%**
Foot size	Small	23	18
	Medium	84	66
	Large	21	16
Hand size	Small	21	16
	Medium	90	70
	Large	17	14

a What correlation do these features show?

b What conclusions can you make about these two features?

c Do you think one feature affects the other? Explain your answer.

3 Strawberry plants can reproduce by runners. New young plants grow on each runner.

a Explain why each new plant is identical to its parent.

b Name three environmental factors that could affect the growth of the young plants.

c What effect would each factor have on growth?

4 A modern pig is descended from the wild boar and there are many species of modern pigs.

a Explain what the word 'species' means.

b Is it possible to make a new species by asexual reproduction? Explain your answer.

c Each species of pig belongs to a genus. Explain what a genus is.

5 Give two differences between plants and animals.

6 Complete the following sentences.
Animals with backbones are called............... Animals without backbones are called............... An arthropod is an............... with legs. Two examples of arthropods are............... and...............

7 Why are snails classified as invertebrates?

8 A number of different animal classes have backbones but they are different from each other. Give two differences between:

a amphibians and mammals

b reptiles and mammals

c birds and mammals

d fish and mammals

e fish and amphibians

f reptiles and amphibians.

9 Choose an animal and a plant and explain three features that make each suited or adapted to its environment. Explain what the effect would be if there were changes in the environment that made that feature less of an advantage.

UNIT 5   The particle theory

Solids, liquids and gases make up the matter all around us. We can tell whether something is a solid, a liquid or a gas, because they behave differently. Some substances, such as water, can exist in all three states.

Some substances can change from a solid to a liquid when we heat them. This is called **melting**. This process is reversed when a liquid cools down and **freezes** to become a solid.

When we heat water it **evaporates** to become a gas called water vapour or steam. When steam cools down, it **condenses** back to water. When water is **frozen** it becomes a solid – ice.

Learning objectives ▶

Reading this unit will help you to know about and understand the following ideas and processes to do with particles and matter:

About the properties of solids, liquids and gases.

That scientists explain difficult ideas using models.

About the particle model of matter.

How the particle theory can be used to explain the properties of solids, liquids and gases.

That the particle theory can explain other things, such as:

- how a wire stretches
- how we smell perfumes in a room
- how a thermometer works.

Key words ▶

atom	expand	matter	state
compress	fluidised bed	model	theory
compressible	force	particle model	vibrate
conductor	implode	pressure	volcanic eruption
diffusion	lava	pressurised	
evidence	magma	properties	

Learning summary ▼

This concept poster summarises the key learning points in this unit.

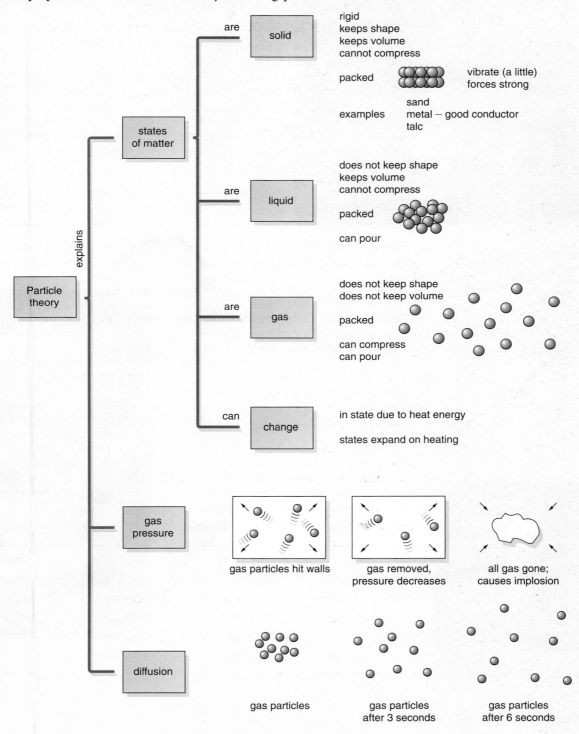

Particle theory — *explains* — **states of matter**

states of matter — *are* — **solid**
- rigid
- keeps shape
- keeps volume
- cannot compress
- packed — vibrate (a little), forces strong
- examples — sand, metal – good conductor, talc

states of matter — *are* — **liquid**
- does not keep shape
- keeps volume
- cannot compress
- packed
- can pour

states of matter — *are* — **gas**
- does not keep shape
- does not keep volume
- packed
- can compress
- can pour

states of matter — *can* — **change**
- in state due to heat energy
- states expand on heating

gas pressure
- gas particles hit walls
- gas removed, pressure decreases
- all gas gone; causes implosion

diffusion
- gas particles
- gas particles after 3 seconds
- gas particles after 6 seconds

Use a concept poster like this to make a summary of other units.

Solids, liquids and gases

5.1 *An erupting volcano throws out solids, liquids and gases*

The Earth is a sphere. It is made up of solids, liquids and gases. We live on a solid outer crust. It is about 40 kilometres thick. This crust floats on liquid rock below. This liquid rock is very, very hot.

In some places on the Earth the crust is weak and sometimes the molten rock below it, known as **magma** or **lava**, can escape. When this happens it is called a **volcanic eruption**.

As the volcano erupts it throws out chunks of rock from its centre. It also releases molten rock from below the Earth's surface and a number of different gases.

The chunks of rock can be thrown large distances. When the large ones land they can cause immense damage. As the molten rock, or lava, comes up from beneath the Earth's surface it flows down the sides of the volcano. The lava has a temperature of about 1000°C, which is hot enough to melt steel.

Volcanoes also give out different gases. Some of these are harmless, such as steam and carbon dioxide. Some are poisonous, such as chlorine and carbon monoxide.

In AD 79 Mount Vesuvius in Italy erupted. Rocks, ash and lava buried the city of Pompeii and its inhabitants. Over 3000 people died. However, they were not all killed by lava and ash. Many died from inhaling the hot poisonous gases from the volcano. Gases spread out and travel much faster than liquids. This meant that the gases reached the people of Pompeii faster than the lava. They were already dead when the lava arrived.

> **1** How are solids, liquids and gases different from each other?

5.2 *A stream of molten lava flowing down a mountain side*

5.3 *Picture from Pompeii exhibition of the man suffocating*

> **2** How do you think this man died?

States of matter

The planet we live on is made up from many different substances, or types of matter. Each of these substances is a solid, a liquid or a gas. These are called the three **states of matter**.

Solids, liquids and gases behave in different ways. The ways in which a substance behaves are sometimes called its properties. Solids, liquids and gases have different **properties**.

A solid such as rock is rigid and keeps its shape. It is easy to measure the volume of a solid. Solids cannot be **compressed**. This means that we cannot squash them.

A liquid such as lava does not have a shape. It can flow. It always takes up the shape of the container it is in. We can measure the volume of a liquid.

A gas has no shape and no volume. It will always fill up the available space and spread out in all directions. This is how gases from volcanoes behave.

5.5 *Flowing lava*

3 What does *volume* mean?

4 What does *rigid* mean?

5.4 *A solid piece of volcanic rock*

5 Make a table showing the properties of solids, liquids and gases.

6 List as many solids, liquids and gases as you can.

Solid or liquid?

Some substances, sand or a bath sponge for example, are difficult to classify. This is because they sometimes show the properties of a solid and sometimes the properties of a liquid.

A careful look at each one is needed to help explain why they behave in this way.

Sand can behave in different ways. When it is wet it is possible to make a rigid shape out of it. It behaves like a solid. However, when it is dry it flows like a liquid does. A closer look at sand shows that it is made up of very small particles. These are called grains.

7 Do you think sand is a solid or a liquid? Explain why.

5.6 *A sand sculpture*

8 Are there other solid substances which can change shape? Explain how this happens.

When the sand is wet the grains stick together. They can be moulded into shapes such as sandcastles. When they are dry they do not stick together and so they can be poured from one container to another. This is because the grains move over one another. The grains flow.

To decide whether sand is a solid or a liquid we must look at an individual grain of sand. It has a fixed shape and a fixed volume so it must be solid. Sand only behaves like a liquid when we look at thousands of grains.

A bath sponge has a rigid shape but when it is squeezed it changes shape. A bath sponge is made up of soft fabric with lots of tiny holes. These holes contain air but when the sponge is put into water they fill up with water. This means that the sponge is not solid all the way through. Pushing the fabric together makes the holes collapse together and the sponge changes shape.

5.7 *How a bath sponge changes shape*

A scientific model

When scientists try to explain something very difficult, they often use a **model**. A model helps us to imagine why different things happen. We can use the model to explain things we cannot see.

It is a little like receiving a birthday present wrapped in paper. It is not possible to see what it is. However, you can often tell a lot about the gift by the feel, the shape and the behaviour of the package. Sometimes it is possible to have a very good guess at what it is!

In other words, it is possible to learn a lot about things even if they cannot be seen.

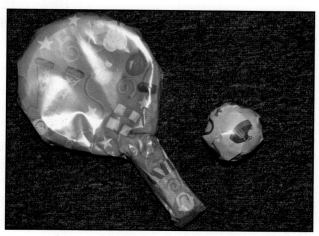

5.8 *What can it be?*

Sometimes new **evidence** is found which the model cannot explain. Scientists may then have to change their original idea to fit the new evidence.

The particle model

We can explain the differences between solids, liquids and gases by using a model. The model explains how solid, liquids and gases behave. It is called the **particle model**. This model is based on evidence collected over hundreds of years by different scientists.

The particle model says that all substances are made up of tiny particles that are too small to see, even with the most powerful microscope. The particles are called **atoms**.

Scientists have built up an idea, or **theory**, of what an atom looks like even though they cannot see one. They have done this by considering all the evidence that they have.

9 What is a model used for in science?

10 What are the clues to the identities of these gifts?

11 How small do you think an atom is?

Find out more about solids, liquids and gases at ▶ **www.scienceweb.co.uk**

HISTORY BOX
Thinking about particles

The Greeks first thought of the concept of atoms as long ago as 400 BC. Leucippus was a famous philosopher and had a pupil called Demokritos. They imagined what would happen if they took a piece of wood and halved it and then halved it again, and again and again. They thought that they would eventually reach a point at which the wood could not be split any more. They said that this was the smallest piece possible.

They called this smallest possible piece of a substance an *atoma*. The word comes from the Greek word meaning indivisible.

The Greeks were not scientists in the way we understand today. They had lots of ideas about how and why things happened, but they did not set about collecting evidence to prove their ideas. They did not carry out experiments.

In the 1800s a teacher called John Dalton performed many scientific experiments. He studied what happened when gases were mixed together. He carefully measured the volume of gases he started with and how much he finished with. He was puzzled when he found that when gases mixed their total volume was less than he expected.

One day he was sitting in his living room and his maid brought in his afternoon tea. He watched her pour the tea into the cup and then add the milk. He saw how they mixed perfectly. Suddenly he had an idea which explained why the tea and the milk mixed so well. They must both be made of tiny particles that could move about and mix together. Dalton said that all substances were made up of particles (atoms).

This was exactly the same idea that the Greek philosophers had had 2000 years before.

John Dalton was a great scientist. He collected evidence carefully but he also had imagination.

Many other scientists of the time thought his ideas about atoms were ridiculous. One scientist wrote, "Atoms are round bits of wood invented by Mr Dalton!" Most scientists had for years been trying to do impossible things, like turning ordinary metals into gold. They had not been concerned with careful observation. Nor had they been concerned with finding patterns and trying to explain what they saw.

12 What does 'indivisible' mean?

13 What do you think happens when gases are mixed?

5.9 *John Dalton thinking about tea*

14 Why do you think some scientists found it hard to believe in particles?

Find out more about particles at ▶ **www.scienceweb.co.uk**

Particles in a solid

In a solid the particles are packed together closely in a regular pattern. The particles are in fixed positions and they cannot move around but they do **vibrate** in these positions. They move forwards and backwards and from side to side. They do not move away from their fixed position.

This explains why, if you place a solid on a table, it stays put. All solids are rigid. They have a fixed shape and a fixed volume.

Solids like rock cannot be squashed. The model says that particles in a solid are packed very closely together in neat rows. If we try to push the particles together there is nowhere for them to move to. There are no spare spaces. This means that solids cannot be squashed together. Solids are not **compressible**.

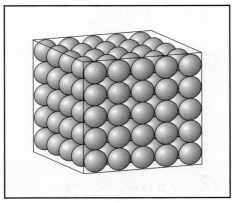

5.10 *In a solid, particles are packed closely together*

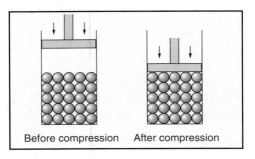

5.11 *Particles in a solid cannot be compressed*

Before compression   After compression

15 Use the model to explain why a rock keeps its shape.

Particles in a liquid

In a liquid, the particles are still close together, but they can move about. They can move past each other.

A liquid will take a shape if it is placed in a container. If the liquid is poured into another container the particles will move around and take up the shape of the new container. However, even though the particles can move around one another, they are still held together. The volume of the liquid stays the same. Liquids do not have a fixed shape but they do have a fixed volume.

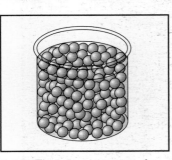

5.12 *The arrangement of particles in a liquid*

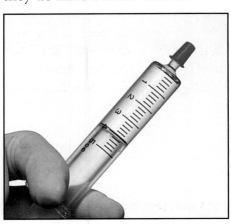

A liquid cannot be heaped up on a table. It always runs away and forms a thin layer. Liquids flow and spread out. Some liquids, such as water, can flow quickly. Other liquids, such as tomato ketchup, flow slowly.

Like solids, liquids cannot be compressed.

5.13 *Liquids cannot be compressed*

16 How are particles in liquids and solids different?

17 Use the particle model to explain why liquids flow.

The particles in a liquid are not arranged in regular patterns. However, they are very close together. This means that if they are squashed together there are no spaces for them to move into.

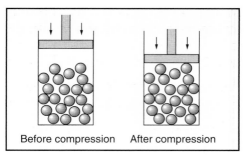

5.14 *Particles in liquids cannot be compressed*

Particles in a gas

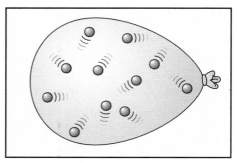

5.15 *Arrangement of particles in a gas*

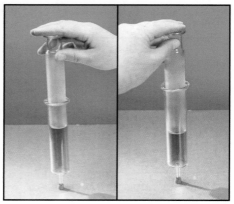

5.16 *Gases can be compressed*

18 How are particles in gases and liquids different?

19 Use the particle model to explain why gases spread out.

In a gas the particles are spread out. They move around a lot. There are big spaces in between them. The particles are not held together and so can move around freely. They can spread in all directions up, down, sideways, forwards and backwards. They can fill both large and small spaces. As the particles are not held together in any way gas does not have a shape or a volume.

Gases spread out to fill all the available space. They fill up all of a container, whatever its size.

Gas particles move through the air. They can be released in one place and travel to another. This process is called **diffusion**. This is why you can smell perfume from an open bottle on the other side of a room.

Because the particles in a gas are so spread out, they can be squashed together. Gases can be compressed.

If the particles in a gas are squashed together there are spaces available for the particles to fit into. However, the particles in a gas have a lot of energy and move around a lot. If gas particles are pushed together they immediately try to move away from each other again. To keep them compressed we need to hold them in the spaces by pushing them together all the time. The gas is then under **pressure** or **pressurised**. Gases are often stored or transported in this way.

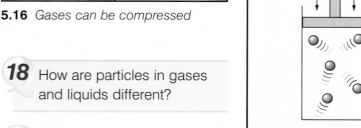

5.17 *Gas particles before compression*

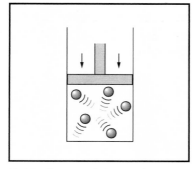

5.18 *Gas particles under pressure*

More gas can be fitted into a container if it is pressurised. This is because more particles can be fitted into a small space. Once the pressure is released the gas particles will immediately move apart again. They will move to fill all the available space.

Aerosol cans contain pressurised gases. When the nozzle is pushed down the pressure is released. This allows the gas particles to escape.

When gases are pressurised they become liquids. This is why, although aerosols release gas, you can hear the sound of liquid inside when an aerosol can is shaken.

5.19 *An aerosol can*

Forces between particles

The particles in a solid are held close together in regular patterns. The forces which hold the particles together are strong.

When small weights are suspended one at a time from a thin wire the wire stretches. If more weights are added the wire will eventually snap.

The wire snaps because the force of the weights pulling down is greater than the attractive force of the particles for each other in the solid.

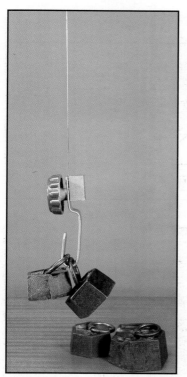

5.20 *Testing the strength of forces between particles*

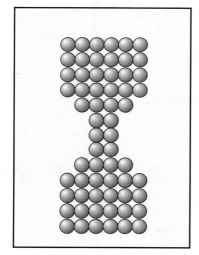

5.21 *Solid particles before the wire snaps*

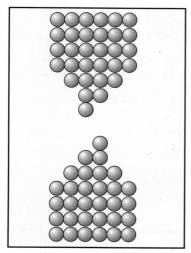

5.22 *Solid particles after the wire snaps*

20 Explain what happens to particles when the wire stretches.

21 Why do you think some solids break more easily than others?

Heating particles

22 Describe how the particles move in a solid, a liquid and a gas.

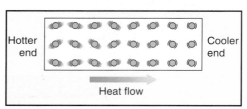

5.23 *The knock-on effect of transfer of energy*

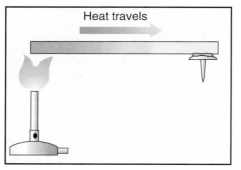

5.24 *The transfer of heat along a metal bar*

23 What does 'expand' mean?

24 Explain why the bar does not fit in the gauge when it has been heated.

25 Why does the liquid move up the thermometer tube when it is heated?

26 Use the particle model to explain what happens to the liquid in a thermometer when it cools down.

The particles which substances are made of can move. They have energy. When a substance is heated it gains energy, which makes the particles vibrate.

In a solid energy is passed from one vibrating particle to another. This is described as a 'knock-on effect'. Some solids, such as metals, are very good at passing on energy. They are good **conductors** of heat.

The effect can be seen if a drawing pin is fixed to one end of a metal bar using grease. The metal bar is heated at the far end. After a few minutes the grease melts and the drawing pin falls off. The heat has travelled from one end of the bar to the other. The energy has passed from particle to particle.

Particles in a solid vibrate more when they are heated. They also try to move away from each other. This means that the distance between the particles increases slightly. The solid **expands**.

We can show this by passing a metal ball through a metal ring. It passes through easily. If the metal ball is heated, it no longer fits through the ring.

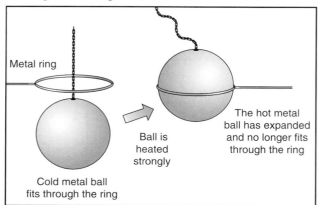

5.25 *A metal ball and ring before and after heating*

Thermometers

A thermometer is used to measure temperature. One type of thermometer is made from liquid sealed in a thin glass tube. When the liquid is heated it expands. The liquid in a thermometer moves up the tube as the temperature rises.

Liquids expand when they are heated. The particles which make up the liquid move further apart as they gain energy.

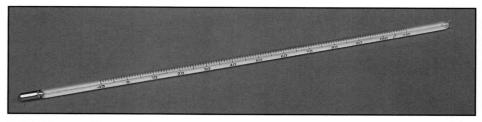

5.26 *Mercury thermometer*

Diffusion

Moving particles spread out in all directions. They keep on spreading until they become evenly distributed. This process is called **diffusion**.

Particles of gas can spread through the air by diffusion. When the lid is left off a perfume jar, particles escape and mix with the gases in the air. The particles move and spread out through the air. You may smell the perfume from a distance because particles have reached your nose.

5.27 *Gas particles spread by diffusion*

When a drop of coloured dye is added to water in a beaker the colour seems to spread out through the water. The particles of the dye are moving through the water and spreading out by diffusion.

When the coloured dye is spread evenly through the water, diffusion ends.

5.28 *Coloured dye diffusing in water*

27 What do you think causes the particles of dye to move through the water?

Gases and pressure

Gas particles move around in all directions with a lot of energy. When they are in a sealed container they move around inside. Some of the particles hit the sides of the container. As the particles hit the sides they push outwards and this causes pressure.

The air particles outside the container are also moving around with a lot of energy. They hit the outside of the container and push inwards. The pressure from the inside of the container equals the pressure from the outside.

The gas particles on the inside can be taken out using a vacuum pump. Now there is no pressure on the inside but there is still pressure from the outside. The container will collapse or **implode**. This is an implosion.

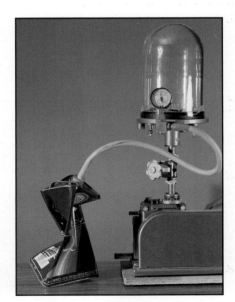

5.31 *External pressure makes an empty container implode*

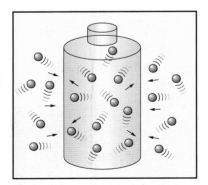

5.29 *Gas particles inside and outside the container create equal pressure*

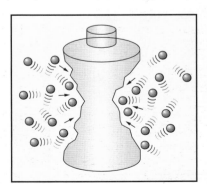

5.30 *The pressure on the outside of an empty container causes an implosion*

28 What happens to the gas particles inside a balloon when you blow it up?

TECHNOLOGY BOX

Fluidised beds

Materials such as talc and sand are solids. However, they can behave like liquids. This is because the tiny individual grains can move over each other, allowing the substance to flow. This can happen to any powder.

In industry, scientists and technologists design ways of making many different materials, for example washing-up liquid, margarine, acid, plastics, fibres, etc.

To make new materials they need to mix together different substances. Sometimes they need to mix together solids and gases. If a large lump of solid needs to be reacted with a gas this can take a long time. However, if the solid is made into a powder and the gas is bubbled through the powder then the reaction happens much more quickly. This is because the gas can reach a lot more of the powder.

In some power stations coal is burned to produce energy. This energy is then used to generate electricity. In some modern power stations a **fluidised bed** of coal is used.

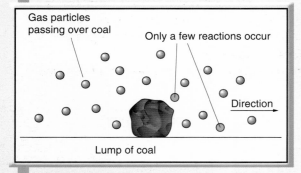

5.32 *A large piece of solid can take longer to fully react*

The coal is powdered into dust. Air is blown through the bed from underneath. This means that lots of coal can burn at once. The coal burns very quickly and there is less pollution than when it is burned in lumps.

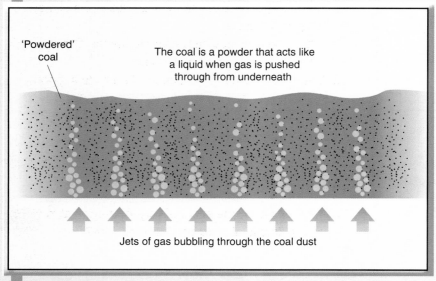

5.33 *A fluidised bed*

29 In what way is a powder like a fluid?

Questions

1 Matter is found in three states – solids, liquids and gases. Each state has differences. Some of these differences are in volume, rigidity and compressibility. This can be explained by the way the particles are arranged.

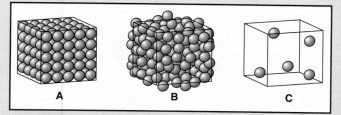

  a Label the diagrams above as solid, liquid and gas.

  b What is volume?

  c Describe how volume is affected by the state of matter.

  d What is rigidity?

  e Describe how rigidity is affected by the state of matter.

  f What is compressibility?

  g Describe how compressibility is affected by the state of matter.

2 Sand appears to act like a liquid.

  a Describe one way in which sand appears to act like a liquid.

  b What characteristics does sand have that makes it possible to classify it as a solid?

  c How would you support the idea that sand is not a liquid?

3 Solids like ice can be changed into a liquid like water and water can change into a gas called steam.

  a Describe how ice can be changed into water and then into steam.

  b What is happening to the particles in ice when it changes state?

  c Describe what is happening to the energy of the particles when ice changes from a solid to steam.

4 Which of these statements are true and which are false?

  a Gas particles stay close together.

  b Dense materials have particles close together.

  c Liquids have particles far apart.

  d Liquids have particles that roll around over each other.

  e There are forces of attraction between particles in a solid.

5 Describe how and why the compressibility of a gas is different from a solid.

6 When gases are compressed they turn into liquids.

  a Give ideas to explain why gases become liquids when they are compressed.

  b These gas/liquids are often put into a container with a cap that can be pressed to release the pressure. Describe what happens when the cap is pressed.

  c What happens to the temperature of the gas when the pressure is released?

7 Draw a diagram to show the arrangement of particles in a:

  a gas

  b liquid

  c solid.

8 Solids have a shape and liquids flow.

  a Explain why the particles in a solid are often arranged and stay in a regular shape.

  b What happens to the particles in a solid when their energy is increased?

  c What would you see happening to the solid?

9 When metals are heated they change in appearance.

  a Explain what happens to the particles in a metal bar when it is heated.

  b What would we see happening to the metal that would help to support that idea?

  c Describe an experiment that would help to support that idea.

10 It is possible to smell perfume some distance from the bottle just after the bottle has been opened.

  a Using the idea of particles, explain why it is possible to smell the perfume.

  b What is the word that describes this process?

  c What would be the effect of very low temperatures on the time it takes to smell the perfume?

UNIT 6 Solutions

Some substances, such as salt or sugar, **dissolve** in water. When they dissolve they mix with the water to make a **solution**. We cannot see the particles of the solid in the solution. Other substances, such as sand or chalk, do not dissolve in water. When a lump of chalk is put into water it sinks to the bottom of the container or floats around in the water.

We can separate solids from liquids by **filtering** or sieving. To get a dissolved solid back from a solution we must **evaporate** the liquid by heating it.

Learning objectives ▶

Reading this unit will help you to know about and understand the following ideas and processes to do with solutions:

The scientific terms we use to describe solutions and dissolving.

How dissolving can be explained using the particle model.

That there is a limit to how much of a solute will dissolve in a solution.

How a solute such as salt can be extracted from a solution by evaporation.

How a solvent such as water can be removed from a solution by distillation.

How small amounts of a dissolved solid can be separated from a solution using chromatography.

That different amounts of some solids may dissolve in water.

That the temperature of the water affects how much of a solute will dissolve.

The uses of different types of solvents.

Key words ▶

alcohol	evaporate	particle model
chromatography	evaporation	residue
condensation	filtering	saturated
condense	filtrate	solubility
condenser	insoluble	soluble
conserved	locating agent	solute
dissolve	mass	solution
distillation	mixture	solvent

Learning summary ▼

This poster summarises the key learning points in this unit.

A solution of cola

- Carbon dioxide   Solute
- Caramel   Solute
- Preservative   Solute
- Water   Solvent

Separation by evaporation

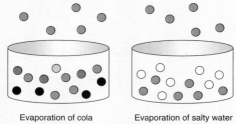

Evaporation of cola   Evaporation of salty water

Dissolving particles

Sugar particles 'stuck' together at start

After some time sugar particles move apart

Same number of particles at end as at start so **mass is conserved**

Saturated solution: no more solute will dissolve at that temperature

No solution of sand and water

- Water
- Sand

Separation by filtering

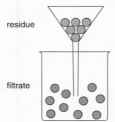

residue

filtrate

Not dissolving particles

Chalk particles 'stuck' together at start

After some time chalk particles still 'stuck' together

Salt extraction

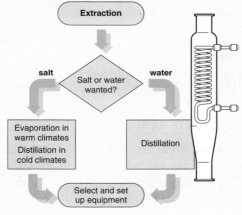

Extraction

salt   Salt or water wanted?   water

Evaporation in warm climates
Distillation in cold climates

Distillation

Select and set up equipment

Chromatography

Used for food colouring and horse doping

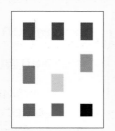

Solvents – examples

Water   Paint cleaner

Nail varnish   Alcohol

Solubility and temperature

Solids – generally more can dissolve at higher temperatures

Gases – generally more can dissolve at lower temperatures

Make a poster to summarise other units.

Popular solutions

Cola is the most popular soft drink in the world. Many companies around the world make cola drinks. Millions of pounds are spent on advertising the different brands, but most of us have our own personal favourite.

6.1 *Different kinds of cola*

Each company has its own secret recipe for how its cola is made. The recipes are guarded very carefully. However, the law in the UK says that all food and drink must list the ingredients they contain on the outside packaging. But companies do not have to reveal the amounts of each ingredient they use. That remains a secret.

Cola drinks are **solutions**. They all begin as water. Many different ingredients are added which **dissolve** in water and make a solution. The drink becomes a **mixture** of different substances. The dissolved substances give the cola its taste and its appearance.

Some of the substances which are dissolved in cola are:

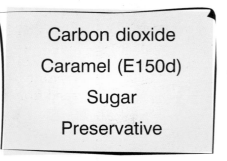

Carbon dioxide

Caramel (E150d)

Sugar

Preservative

Cola drinks are made to strict recipes. The same amount of each ingredient is always put into the water. However, different colas are made up differently. They have different amounts of each solute in them. This is why different brands of cola have slightly different tastes.

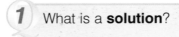

1 What is a **solution**?

6.2 *Ingredients label from a cola drink*

2 What does each of these ingredients do in the cola drink?

Soluble and insoluble substances

Substances that dissolve in water are called **soluble** substances. The ingredients in a cola drink are soluble. They dissolve to make a solution which is clear. We cannot see any bits of solid in the solution although sometimes it may be coloured.

6.3 *A glass of cola*

Some substances do not dissolve in water. They are called **insoluble** substances. When an insoluble solid is put into water the bits of solid sink to the bottom of the container or float around. The mixture may look 'cloudy'. The insoluble substance forms a suspension in the liquid.

The table below shows some substances which are soluble and some which are insoluble in water.

Soluble substances	Insoluble substances
Salt	Sand
Sugar	Chalk
Copper sulphate	Copper carbonate

3 How can you tell whether a substance is soluble in water?

4 How can you tell whether a substance is insoluble in water?

5 Write down two more substances for each group.

Separating mixtures

6.5 *Filtering a suspension*

You can separate an insoluble solid from a liquid by **filtering**. When it is filtered the solid is trapped in the filter paper. This is the **residue**. The liquid that drips through is the **filtrate**.

In a science lesson, Ana and Jo designed a way of separating sand from the salt in rock salt. First they added the rock salt to water in a beaker. The salt dissolved. They filtered the mixture to separate the bits of sand from the salt solution.

6.4 *A cloudy suspension – chalk and water*

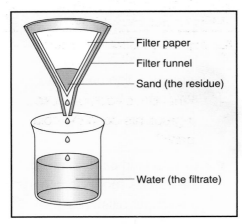

Filter paper
Filter funnel
Sand (the residue)
Water (the filtrate)

6.6 *Apparatus used in filtering*

6.7 *Evaporating salt water over a burner*

6 What happened when the water evaporated?

6.9 *This drink is a mixture of solutes*

7 Make a table to summarise the information about these three drinks.

8 How are the particles arranged differently in a solid and a liquid?

9 Draw a strip cartoon using the particle model to show how sugar dissolves in water.

You cannot separate the parts of a solution such as cola by filtering. All the dissolved substances would pass through the filter paper along with the water.

However, you can get the dissolved substances back from the solution. To do this you must heat the solution. The water will eventually **evaporate**. The solids are then left behind.

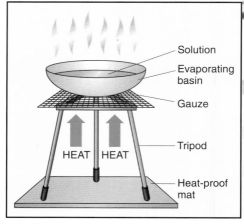

6.8 *Apparatus used for evaporating*

Ana and Jo collected the filtrate from their rock salt investigation in a dish. They heated the dish with a burner to evaporate the water.

Solutes and solvents

A substance that dissolves in a liquid, such as salt, is called a **solute**. The liquid part of a solution is called a **solvent**. Solutions are made when solutes and solvents are mixed together.

A solvent is a liquid which will dissolve a solid. Water is the most common solvent in the world.

When sugar dissolves in tea, the sugar is the solute. The tea is the solvent. The sweet cup of tea is the solution.

When carbon dioxide dissolves in water, the carbon dioxide is the solute. The water is the solvent. The fizzy water is the solution.

When coffee granules dissolve in boiling water, the coffee granules are the solute. The water is the solvent. The cup of coffee is the solution.

The particle model and dissolving

The **particle model** can explain how solutes dissolve in solvents.

A solid solute, such as sugar, has particles in neat, regular rows. A solvent, such as water, is a liquid. It has particles that are close together and that move about.

When a lump of sugar is placed in the water, the water particles move in between the solid particles and push them apart. The sugar particles are pushed further and further apart. They break away from each other and mix with the water particles. When they spread through the water they cannot be seen as a solid lump. The sugar has dissolved.

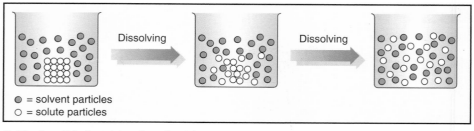

6.10 *A solid dissolving in a liquid*

When 10 cm³ of sugar is added to 100 cm³ of water, the final volume of the mixture is not 110 cm³. It is slightly less. This is because the sugar particles fit in the spaces between the water particles.

We can explain how this might happen using a different model.

If a beaker full of sand is added to a beaker full of peas, the sand grains fill in the gaps between the peas. The grains of sand act like the particles of sugar. The dried peas act like the particles of water.

The model also shows that all the sugar that is added stays in the container. All the water that is added is also still there. This means that the **mass** of the two substances together must still be the same.

Measuring the mass of the sugar and the mass of the water before they are mixed can prove this. The final mass of the solution is the sum of the two. This means that nothing has disappeared. The mass is **conserved**.

6.11 *Sugar and water before and after mixing, with mass indicated*

6.12 *Sand and peas, before mixing*

10 What do the peas and beans represent in this model? What will happen when they are mixed?

11 Some people think that a substance disappears when it dissolves. How does the evidence of mass disprove this idea?

The particle model and insoluble substances

When an insoluble substance, such as sand, is mixed with water it does not dissolve. This is because when the solvent and the substance are mixed, the particles of solvent cannot push the particles of substance apart.

The forces holding the solid particles together are too strong for the solvent particles to break them apart. The solvent particles cannot get in between them.

12 Explain why sand cannot dissolve in water.

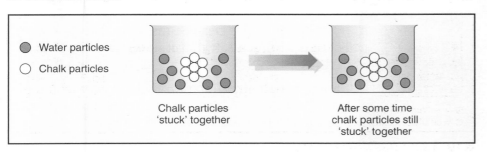

6.13 *The particles of the solvent cannot push the solid particles apart to form a solution*

Why won't any more sugar dissolve?

13 What is a saturated solution?

14 Why can no more solute be dissolved in a saturated solution?

Saturated solutions

At home, Ana was making a cup of tea for her mother. She added lots of spoonfuls of sugar to the tea. She noticed that after a while no more sugar would dissolve in the tea.

When a solvent will not let any more solute dissolve in it we say that it is a **saturated** solution.

The particle model can also explain why only a certain amount of solute will dissolve in a solvent.

There are only so many spaces for the solute particles to fit into. This means that once they are filled no more solute particles can fit in. The solution is saturated.

6.14 *The high seas*

The seas and oceans

One of the most common substances on earth is salt. Its chemical name is sodium chloride. It is found as rock salt in the ground and as a solute in the seas and oceans.

All the seas and oceans contain dissolved salt. The amount is usually about 30 g of salt to each litre of water. One litre of water has a mass of 1000 g. This means that about 3% of the ocean is salt by weight. The sea also contains many other solutes. These include sodium bromide, magnesium chloride, calcium carbonate and magnesium sulphate.

In different parts of the world there are different amounts of these solutes in the sea water.

15 Why do you think people can float in the Dead Sea?

For example, in the Dead Sea there is a lot more salt than in other seas and oceans. The amount of salt is about 300 g per litre of water. This means that about 30% of the Dead Sea is salt by weight, ten times more than in the other oceans and seas.

The water in the Dead Sea is a saturated solution. There is so much salt that it is very easy to float in it.

Some people find flotation therapy very relaxing. Many cities have relaxation centres where people can float in a tank of salty water for an hour or so.

6.15 *Floating in the Dead Sea*

HISTORY BOX

The history of salt

Salt is very important to us. Our bodies need salt so that our muscles and brain can work properly. It also helps cuts to heal well.

Nowadays, a well-balanced diet provides us with all the salt we need.

The salt that we use today is either mined from underground or taken from the sea. Two hundred million years ago much of the UK was covered by sea. The climate then was very hot and the sea water eventually evaporated. The salt was left behind.

Many layers of clay and sand then covered the salt. However in Cheshire and other parts of central and northern England, the salt is near the surface and can be mined.

Many years ago salt was particularly important to people because it could be used to preserve food (keep it fresh). People did not have tinned food, or refrigerators or freezers to keep food fresh. If they treated food with salt it prevented it from going bad. Roman soldiers were actually partly paid in salt. This is where the word 'salary' comes from. *Sal* is the Latin for salt. *Salarium* means salary in Latin.

Salt is so important that wars have been fought over it. If tribes had salt they could treat the food they gathered in the summer and autumn and keep it for the winter, when food supplies were scarce. This kept the tribe from starving. Some people were even prepared to exchange people for salt.

In the 18th and 19th centuries salt was first used to make other chemicals. The chemical name for salt is sodium chloride. Lots of important materials can be made from it. Today salt is a very important raw material for many manufacturing processes.

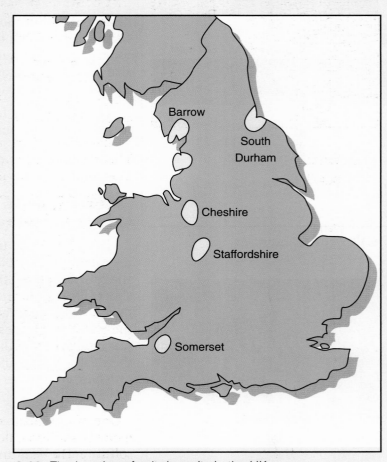

6.16 *The location of salt deposits in the UK*

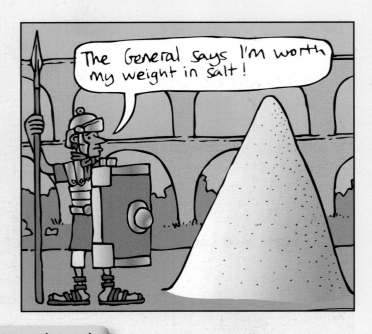

Find out more about salt on the Internet at ▶ **www.scienceweb.co.uk**

Extracting salt

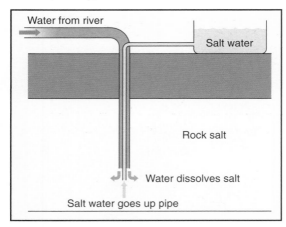

6.17 *Rock salt extraction*

6.18 *Collecting salt from a salt bed*

16 How was rock salt formed?

17 Write a sentence to describe what is going on in each stage of this process.

Salt is a very important chemical. It is a compound containing sodium and chlorine. Salt is needed for many things. It is used in cooking and it is put on the roads in winter to stop them freezing. It is also used to make other important chemicals like hydrogen, chlorine and sodium hydroxide.

In Britain, salt is found underground in rocks and is called rock salt. It is extracted by pumping water down into the salt layers. The salt dissolves and forms salt solution. This salt solution is sometimes called brine. The brine is then pumped back to the surface and the salt is obtained by evaporating the water.

In other countries around the world, salt can be obtained in different ways. It can be extracted from sea water, swamp water or plants.

Sea water can be used as a cheap source of salt. Many hot countries use sea water to obtain their salt. Sea water is pumped into huge shallow lakes near the shore. Heat from the Sun then slowly evaporates the water and leaves the salt behind. The salt is then gathered up and transported to where it is needed.

The process of extracting salt from rock salt can also be done in the laboratory. The same chemical principles are used. However, the method is different. This is because the extraction is being done on a much smaller scale.

The flow chart on the right shows how salt is extracted from rock salt in the laboratory.

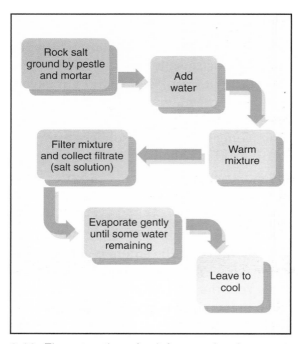

6.19 *The extraction of salt from rock salt*

Getting the water back

In many parts of the world there is a shortage of fresh water for drinking and washing. In hot countries near the sea people sometimes use sea water for their drinking water. To do this they first need to remove the salt. The salt and water are separated by heating the sea water.

The sea water is heated in a **desalination plant** until the water evaporates using energy from the Sun. The water vapour is collected and then cooled. This causes the water vapour to **condense**. It turns into pure liquid water. This process of **evaporation** followed by **condensation** is called **distillation**.

Distillation needs to be carried out on a large scale to provide enough drinking water for a town or city. It also needs to be done as cheaply as possible. This is why energy from the Sun is used to evaporate the water.

We can separate the water from a solution on a small scale in the laboratory using **distillation**.

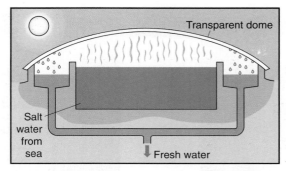

6.20 *How a simple desalination plant works*

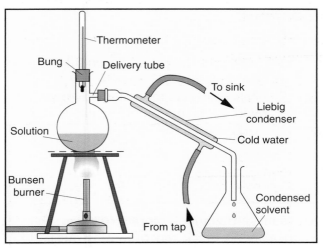

6.21 *Distillation using a condenser*

The image on the left shows the apparatus that is used for distillation in the laboratory. It is called a condenser.

The solution is heated in a flask until it boils. The solvent evaporates into a gas and the gas rises. The gas travels into the condenser. There is a cold water jacket surrounding the glass tubing in the middle of the condenser. This makes the tube in the middle cold. As the gas enters the tube it cools down. It then condenses back into a liquid. The liquid runs down the tube and is collected. The solute stays behind in the flask.

18 What does desalination mean?

19 What happens during the process of condensation?

20 Draw a flow diagram showing how a condenser works.

Separating small amounts of solute in solvents

Sometimes the amount of solute dissolved in the solvent is very small. The amounts are so small that separating them by distillation does not work. If this is the case, **chromatography** can be used.

Chromatography

Coloured inks and dyes are often made by dissolving different coloured chemicals into solvents. Usually there are only small amounts of each colour present in the dye. It is possible to separate out the colours and find out which ones are present. This is done using a method called chromatography.

For example, green food colouring could be made by using a single green colour. However, it could also be made by mixing blue and yellow dyes together.

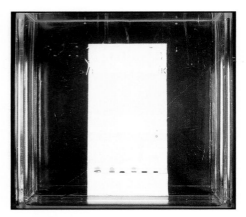

6.22 *Chromatography set up*

21 What colour do you think the inks in Figure 6.23 were?

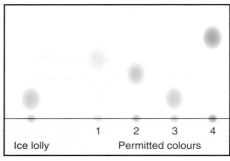

6.24 *Chromatography can be used to see what colourings are in an ice lolly*

22 What does this chromatogram tell you about the colourings used in different lollies?

23 When is a locating agent used?

Figure 6.23 shows how coloured inks can be tested to find out what pigments they contain.

A strip of absorbent paper is used. The ink or dye is spotted onto the bottom part of the paper. The paper is then hung in a solvent. The spot must not be allowed to hang under the level of the surface of the solvent. The paper is left for a short time.

The solvent soaks up the paper. When it reaches the spot of ink or dye the dye dissolves in the solvent. The solvent carries the particles of dye up the paper. If the particles are light they are carried easily by the solvent and so are carried a long way. If the particles are larger, they are carried slowly by the solvent and do not spread so far.

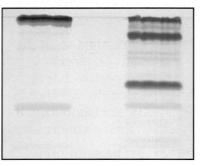

The particles spread out as they travel up the paper, depending on their size. We can see the colours separate. Eventually they will reach the top of the paper and they can be collected.

6.23 *Chromatogram of two coloured inks*

Testing food colouring

Many foods are coloured to make them look more attractive. A common yellow dye is tartrazine. A quick way of finding out if tartrazine is in a food us to look at the label on the packet. The code for tartrazine is E102. Some people are allergic to tartrazine and need to know if it is present in a food. If the manufacturer had used the wrong dye it could make them ill.

Food scientists working for the government regularly check to ensure that the labels on foods are accurate. They use chromatography to separate substances dissolved in food. They identify which solutes are present.

Figure 6.24 shows how chromatography can be used to check what colourings there are in an orange ice lolly.

Invisible clues

The substances separated by chromatography do not have to be coloured. Many substances in solutions are not coloured. Some colourless substances can be made to show up by spraying the paper with a **locating agent**. The locating agent reacts with each of the colourless substances to form a coloured product. We can then find where they are on the paper.

For example, in horse racing horses are sometimes given drugs to make them go faster. This is illegal. Horses are often tested after a race to see if they have been given these drugs.

A sample of the horse's urine is taken and tested to see if it contains traces of forbidden drugs. Chromatography is used again. A solvent separates the substances dissolved in the horse's urine.

As the substances involved are not coloured a **locating agent** is used. This shows which substances are present in the urine. The scientist can identify if any of these are forbidden drugs.

Measuring solubility

Not all substances dissolve in equal amounts in a solvent like water. Different solutes will dissolve in different amounts. How easily a substance dissolve in a solvent is called its **solubility**. Each substance has a different solubility. A substance with a high solubility will dissolve easily.

We can compare the solubility of different substances by seeing how much will dissolve in 100 g of water, a quantity that is always used to ensure that the comparison of solubility is fair.

This table shows how soluble some substances are.

Solute	How many grams dissolve in 100 g of water at 20°C?
Salt	36
Sugar	211
Copper sulphate	21

24 Draw a graph to show these data.

25 Which substance has the highest solubility? Which has the lowest?

Solubility and temperature

Solubility is affected by other things. We usually wash clothes by putting them in water. The water cannot dissolve all the dirt on the clothes so soap is used.

The water used is usually warm or hot water. This is because hot water dissolves the dirt more easily than the cold water. Hot water also dissolves more dirt than cold water. This is true with most solvents and solutes. The hotter the solvent, the more solute will dissolve in it.

We can test this by trying to dissolve as much solute as possible in 100 g of water at different temperatures.

The table below shows the mass in grams of the solute which can be dissolved in 100 g of water to give a saturated solution at different temperatures. More and more solute can dissolve as the temperature of the solvent increases.

This information can also be plotted as a graph.

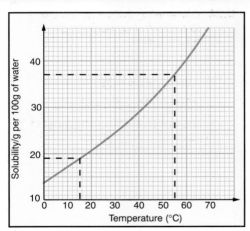

6.25 *Solubility curve for copper (II) sulphate*

26 Which substance is the most soluble at 0°C?

27 Which is the most soluble at 100°C?

Solute	0°C	10°C	20°C	40°C	60°C	80°C	100°C
Ammonium chloride	29	33	37	46	55	66	77
Copper sulphate	14	17	21	29	40	55	75
Potassium nitrate	13	21	32	64	110	169	246

TECHNOLOGY BOX

Different solvents

Water is often called the universal solvent because so many substances dissolve in it. There are many other different solvents which can be used to do different jobs.

Nail varnish removers often contain a solvent called propanone. Propanone is very good at dissolving nail varnish.

Paint brush cleaners contain a solvent called white spirit. White spirit dissolves gloss paint.

Perfume sprays use alcohol as a solvent. The pure perfume is dissolved in alcohol. When the perfume is sprayed onto warm skin, the alcohol evaporates and the perfume is released.

Sometimes clothes are not washed in water. They are sent to the dry cleaner. Dry cleaning uses other solvents that do not contain water. These are called non-aqueous solvents. Non-aqueous solvents generally dissolve grease and oil better than water does. A dry-cleaning machine is like a washing machine but it uses a non-aqueous solvent instead of water. Because the solvent is expensive, it is distilled and reused rather than thrown away.

6.26 *Removing nail varnish*

6.27 *A dry-cleaning machine*

Questions

1 A beaker is put on a top pan balance. Water is added to the beaker and the mass is 250 g. 20.75 g of salt is added to the water and the mixture carefully stirred.

   a What is the mass of the salt in water?

   b What happens to the volume of water after the salt has been added and the mixture stirred? Explain why this happens?

   20 g of sand is added to the water and salt mixture on the top pan balance.

   c What is the new mass of the water, salt and sand mixture?

   d What happens to the volume of the mixture? Explain your answer.

2 Pete wants to separate a mixture of copper sulphate and copper carbonate. He knows copper sulphate will dissolve easily in warm water and copper carbonate will not. Describe how Pete would go about separating the two compounds.

3 A car has knocked down a pedestrian. The police find some paint from the car on the pedestrian's clothes. They are able to separate the paint into its different pigments using a special technique. There are four suspect cars. Samples are collected from each of these and tests carried out. The results are below.

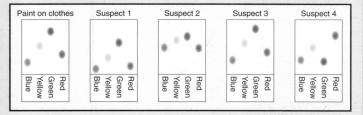

   a Which suspect could be the guilty party? Explain your answer.

   b What is this process called?

   c Which pigment is exactly the same in more than one of the suspect car's paint samples? Explain your answer.

4 Boiling water is poured onto a teabag. It is observed every 20 seconds for 5 minutes. The colour of the water changes steadily for 210 seconds and then it is constant.

   a Explain how teabags work and why the water turns brown when hot water is poured onto the teabag.

   b Draw a graph to describe the changes seen as the teabag remains in the water.

   c Give two ways in which you could change the rate of colour release.

5 A sugar crystal is placed in a container of boiling water.

   a Explain what happens to the crystal in the boiling water.

   b Draw diagrams and describe what happens to the particles in the solid.

6 Darren and Bailey investigate how an unknown coloured substance dissolves. They add 1 g quantities until no more will dissolve. They repeat this for five different temperatures. The results are below.

Temperature	Quantity dissolved
10	15 g
20	20 g
30	32 g
40	39 g
50	
60	50 g
70	52 g
80	53 g

   a Draw a graph of the results.

   b Work out the missing value.

   c Why do you think the values flatten off?

   d When you reach the point where no more will dissolve what type of solution has been formed?

7 Describe how distillation works. Draw and label a diagram of distillation apparatus.

UNIT 7 Acids and alkalis

Many different materials **dissolve** in water and other liquids to form **solutions**. Different materials have different **properties**. This means they behave in different ways.

Sometimes mixing materials results in a new material being formed. This is called a **chemical reaction**. Chemical reactions are irreversible.

Acids are substances that have special properties in common. Some acids are dangerous and must be handled carefully.

Learning objectives ▶

Reading this unit will help you to know about and understand the following ideas and processes to do with acids and alkalis:

That acids and alkalis are important solutions in our everyday lives.

About the properties and uses of acids and alkalis.

That acids and alkalis behave as opposites to each other.

To be able to identify an acid by its properties and interaction with an indicator.

About indicators and how indicators are used to identify acids and alkalis.

That the pH scale measures the strength of acids or alkalis.

That acids and alkalis can react and cancel each other out (neutralisation).

About some uses of neutralisation in our lives.

Key words ▶

acid	corrosive	neutral	pH scale
acidic	hydrochloric acid	neutralisation	solution
alkali		neutralise	sulphuric acid
alkaline	indicator	nitric acid	universal indicator
caustic	litmus	pH meter	
	mineral acid		

Learning summary ▽

This word list summarises the key learning points in this unit.

Word/term	Definition (what it means) and/or examples
Acid	An example of a common acid is citric acid, found in lemon juice and orange juice. Examples of mineral acids are sulphuric, nitric and hydrochloric acid. Acid uses: car batteries and pickling food
Alkali	Examples of common alkalis are soap, toothpaste, indigestion tablets and some cleaning products
Corrosion	The material is eaten away because of a chemical reaction. Example: metal and skin in contact with acid
Hazchem	A code to give information on how to deal with chemicals. Used by fire fighters
Indicator	A liquid that changes colour when added to an acid or alkali. Example: litmus which is red in acid and blue in alkali
Neutralisation	Acid and alkali cancel each other out. The pH becomes 7. Examples are: toothpaste versus acid from bacteria and indigestion tablets versus stomach acid. Also used to adjust soil pH
pH scale	The liquid changes colour depending on the strength of the acid or alkali. Red shows strong acid and purple strong alkali
Strong acid	When a few million molecules of acid are added to water they all break apart. The pH will be 1 or 2
Weak acid	When a few million molecules of acid are added to water some of them will break apart. The pH will be 4–6
Word equation	Says in words what you put into the reaction (on the left before the arrow) and what you got out of the reaction (on the right after the arrow). Three examples are: acid + metal → salt + hydrogen acid + carbonate → salt + water + carbon dioxide acid + alkali → salt + water

Make word lists to summarise other units.

Acid attack!

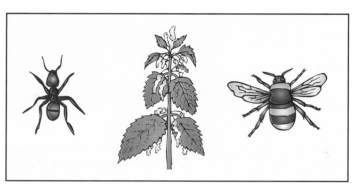

7.1 *Stinging organisms*

7.2 *An extracted bee sting*

1 What might an animal hope to find in a bees' nest?

2 Why do you think nettles have stings?

3 Which foods have citric acid added to them?

Have you ever been bitten by an ant? Or stung by a bee? Or fallen into some nettles and been covered with a painful rash? If the answer is 'yes', then you have been attacked by chemicals called **acids** made by living things. Many plants and animals use acids to protect themselves against danger. The acid is usually injected by a sting or a bite.

Some ants make an acid that they can squirt at their enemies. They will do this if their nest is in danger from predators. Biting ants leave a little of the acid under the skin of their victim. The acid is irritating and painful.

Bees have a sting at the rear end of their bodies. The sting is fed with acid stored in a bag inside the bee's body. Bees will sting other animals to protect their hive when it is in danger. The sharp sting is pushed into the animal's skin and acid pumped in. When a human is stung in this way it often means death for the bee, however. The bee cannot always pull the sting out again, and when it tries the sting itself is ripped off leaving the injured bee to die.

Stinging nettles also contain acid. The acid is contained in tiny bags in hair-like cells that cover the leaves and stem. When a creature brushes against these cells the acid is released onto the skin. It can cause a painful rash.

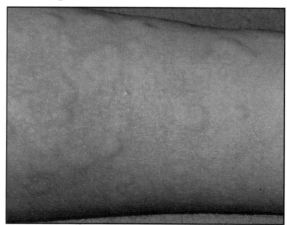

7.3 *Rash caused by a nettle sting*

Although acid stings can be very annoying, other acids are very useful. There are many common acids which we use everyday. Many foods contain acid. Vinegar, oranges and lemons are examples. The acid gives these foods a sharp taste which we can recognise instantly as **acidic**. Some man-made foods have citric acid added to them to give them a 'zingy' taste.

Common acids

Acids are usually **solutions**. Most are clear and look like water. Many of the acids we find around us, such as those in foods, are harmless. Soft drinks such as lemonade and colas have carbon dioxide gas dissolved in them. This is what makes them 'fizz'. This gas also makes them acidic. If a dirty coin is place in a glass of cola, the dirt is soon cleaned from it. Even though they might look innocent, it is NEVER safe to taste a solution to find out whether it is acidic or not. Some acids have very dangerous properties.

Harmful acids usually have a special sign on them. They are **corrosive,** which means they attack metals, reacting with them and eating them away. They can also attack our skin, eyes, mouths, stomach and other tissue, so they must be handled carefully. These acids are often called **mineral acids** because they are made from natural rocks or minerals. They include **sulphuric** acid, **nitric** acid and **hydrochloric** acid.

Although they are dangerous these acids are also very useful. They are used in batteries, and in industry they are used in many processes to make other materials.

Some acids we meet everyday are shown below.

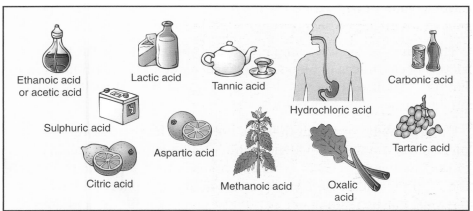

Ethanoic acid or acetic acid

Lactic acid

Tannic acid

Carbonic acid

Sulphuric acid

Hydrochloric acid

Aspartic acid

Tartaric acid

Citric acid

Methanoic acid

Oxalic acid

Acids can kill cells or prevent them working properly. This can make them dangerous to handle. However, this property of acids can be useful. Acids can kill bacteria in foods. Vinegar is ethanoic acid and pickling in vinegar is an ancient way of preserving food. It makes the food taste sour but many people like this taste. This means we still pickle some foods although we now have lots of other ways of preserving them.

7.6 *Pickled onions*

---

4 What is a solution?

7.4 *A dirty coin being cleaned in a glass of cola*

5 How does cola clean dirty coins?

CORROSIVE

7.5 *Hazard symbol for acids*

6 Make a list of those acids which are found in foods.

7 What is this rhyme about?

8 What other foods can be preserved by pickling?

HISTORY BOX

How to dispose of a murder victim!

7.7 *John George Haigh*

7.8 *Haigh following his arrest*

9 Are there other substances which acid does not attack?

John George Haigh was one of Britain's most notorious criminals in the last century. He committed a series of murders which he believed would be impossible to detect. But he was betrayed by the acid he used.

He killed six people who had become his friends. He then put their bodies in a bath of acid. The acid ate away the bodies almost entirely. His first victims were all members of the same family. Having killed them he took everything they had. He forged documents and took over their houses and belongings. No one suspected anything and the disappearances were never reported.

Haigh then became friendly with a doctor and his wife. In December 1947 he ordered two 40-gallon drums of sulphuric acid to be delivered to his workshop. He lured the doctor and his wife to his workshop where he killed them both. He then placed both bodies in the acid drums. Once again he forged documents and sold the doctor's house and car. By now Haigh was very well-off.

His final victim was a wealthy widow. One February afternoon he invited her to his workshop and shot her dead. He stole her money and jewellery, and dropped her body into another vat of acid. Once again the acid destroyed the body completely.

Suspicions were aroused by this final murder, however. The police moved in quickly to search Haigh's workshop.

The search of his workshop revealed a cleaner's ticket for the victim's coat, traces of blood on the walls and a revolver hidden in a hat box. Haigh was not worried at all. He told the police "You can't prove murder without a body."

Unfortunately for Haigh this was not true. The police found one piece of incriminating evidence which Haigh could not explain. A set of the victim's false teeth, which were made from a plastic resin, were found in the bath, together with some bone fragments and fatty remains. Plastic resin is one substance which sulphuric acid does not destroy!

Haigh was found guilty of murder at his trial at the Old Bailey and sentenced to death. He was hanged at Wandsworth Prison on 6th August 1949.

Find out more about the acid bath murders at ▶ **www.scienceweb.co.uk**

Alkalis

Alkalis are the chemical opposites of acids. They are also usually solutions. There are many common alkalis in use everyday. They are powerful substances. Many cleaning products contain alkalis. They are also found in the laboratory and are used in industry.

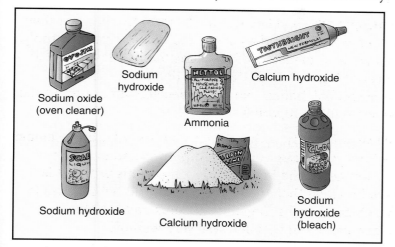

Like acids, some alkalis are very dangerous. They are described as **caustic** which means that they can burn the skin. A splash of sodium hydroxide in the eye can blind someone. These alkalis usually have a special sign on them. Alkalis often feel 'soapy' on the skin. However, you should NEVER use touch as a way of testing to see if a substance is alkali.

In industry alkalis are used in making many important materials.

Many alkalis are used in cleaning products. Like acids, alkalis can also kill bacteria. However, alkalis can also react with grease and help remove it. Mild alkalis are used in shampoos and soaps. Stronger alkalis are used in oven cleaners and bleaches.

This label from a bleach bottle gives lots of information to the user. It lists precautions that should be taken when using bleach. It warns about the dangers of bleach and what to do in the case of an accident. The warning sign is very clear and eye-catching.

Handling acids and alkalis

Strong acids and alkalis need to be handled with great care in the laboratory.

Precautions include:
- wearing goggles/safety glasses
- wearing gloves
- ensuring that the stopper is replaced each time acid is poured from the bottle
- placing the container on a small dish or in a glass trough
- wearing protective overalls
- ensuring there is an acid-resistant surface on the laboratory bench.

7.9 *Hazard symbol for alkalis*

10 Why would it be dangerous to test an alkali by touching it?

WARNING

IRRITANT

Contains Sodium Hypochlorite Solution, available chlorine 4.5% w/w.
Contact with acids liberates toxic gas.
Irritating to eyes and skin.
Keep out of reach of children.
Avoid contact with skin and eyes.

Keep upright in a cool place.
In case of contact with eyes rinse immediately with plenty of water and seek medical advice.
After contact with skin, wash immediately with plenty of water. If swallowed seek medical advice immediately and show this container.
Keep only in original container.
DO NOT reuse this bottle.

7.10 *Bleach label*

11 Explain why one of the precautions is 'Keep only in original container.'

12 How does placing the container on a small dish help keep an acid safe in the lab?

Using indicators to test for acids and alka

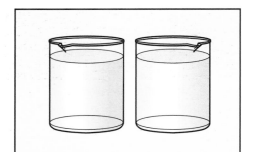

7.11 *Which is the acid and which is the alkali?*

13 What is lichen?

7.12 *The litmus solution test*

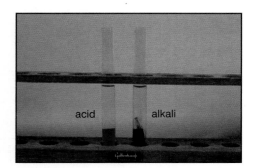

7.13 *Testing with litmus paper*

14 Which indicator has been used here?

Acids and alkalis have some things in common with each other:

- they are both usually solutions
- they are both colourless
- they can both be very harmful.

So how can we tell them apart?

A safe and accurate test of whether a solution is an acid or an alkali is to use an **indicator**. This is a special substance that changes colour depending on whether it is mixed with an acid or an alkali.

Indicators are often made from juices extracted from plants. A common indicator used in schools is **litmus**. Litmus is made from substances extracted from lichen. Litmus turns red in an acid and blue in an alkali.

A few drops of the indicator in the test solution will indicate whether the solution is an acid or an alkali.

Some other plant juices can be used as indicators.

Name of plant	Colour in acid	Colour in alkali
Red cabbage	Red	Blue
Bluebells	Blue	Green

In the laboratory we use indicators that have already been prepared.

Indicator	Colour in acid	Colour in alkali
Litmus	Red	Blue
Methyl orange	Red	Yellow
Phenol phthalein	Colourless	Pink

In school you may use strips of paper which have been soaked in an indicator and dried.

> *Lemon juice contains citric acid. It is described as being 'acidic'.*
>
> *Sodium hydroxide is an alkali. It is described as being 'alkaline'.*
>
> *The words ' acid' and 'alkali' are nouns.*
>
> *The words 'acidic' and 'alkaline' are adjectives.*

Universal indicator and the pH scale

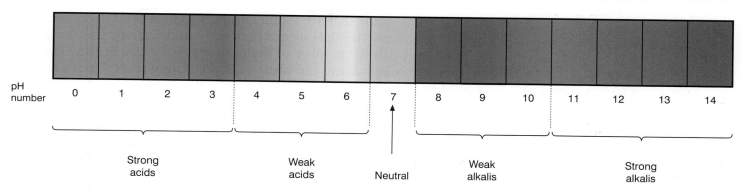

7.14 *A colour chart of the pH scale*

Acids and alkalis are not all the same. Some are much stronger than others. An indicator such as litmus will only tell us if the solution is an acid or an alkali. It will not tell us of how strong the acid or alkali is. To do this we need a special indicator called **universal indicator**. This is a mixture of different indicators.

Universal indicator changes colour according to how strong or weak an acid or alkali is. These colours form the **pH scale**. The full range of the scale runs from pH 1 to pH 14 and characteristic colours represent each number on the pH scale. pH 7 is **neutral**. It is neither alkaline nor acidic. Water is a neutral liquid.

Universal indicator can be a solution. A few drops are added to the test solution. The resulting colour is then checked against the pH colour chart.

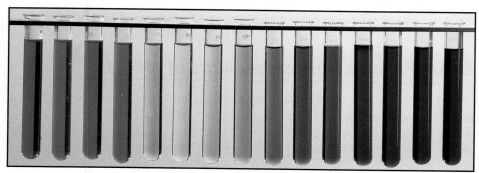

7.15 *Colour on the pH scale*

15 Why is universal indicator more useful than litmus?

It can also be used as strips of paper. A small drop of the test solution is dotted on to the paper. The colour on the paper is then compared to the pH chart.

Find out more about the pH scale at ▶ **www.scienceweb.co.uk**

Strong and weak acids

Food	pH
Molasses	5
Dried apricots	4
Grapefruit	3
Lemon	2

Usually the acids that are found naturally in fruits and vegetables are weak acids. They have pH values between 4 and 6. Their solutions contain only a small number of the particles that cause acidity. The mineral acids, sulphuric and nitric acid, are strong acids. Their pH values are between 1 and 3.

If we know the pH of a solution, we can compare the acidity of one solution to another. Look at the pH values of the foods shown in the table on the left.

What do the numbers mean?

Each one-unit change in pH increases the strength of the acid by a factor of 10.

- A unit change from pH 5 to pH 4 would cause a 10× increase in acidity.

- A unit change from pH 5 to pH 3 would be a hundred times (100×) increase in acidity.

Dried apricots have a pH of 4 – this means that they are 10 times more acidic than molasses which has a pH of 5.

Grapefruit has a pH of 3 – this means it is 10 times more acidic than dried apricots and 100 times (100×) more acidic than molasses.

16 What is the difference in strength of the lemon compared to each of the other foods?

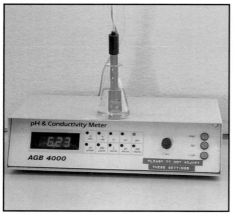

7.16 *Testing solutions using a pH meter with a digital reading*

Making accurate measurements of pH

The pH scale is a continuous scale. Acids and alkalis can have pHs that have decimal points. To find the exact pH of a substance it is more accurate to use a **pH meter**. This uses a probe that is placed in the test solution. The exact pH is then registered on the read-out scale. The scale can be analogue or digital.

The pH of the foods in the table was tested using a pH meter.

For some substances, such as blackcurrants or other coloured food, the only accurate way to measure acidity is with a meter.

Food	pH
Lime	1.7
Lemon	2.3
Cabbage	5.3
Apple	3.1
Grapes	4.0
Bread	5.5
Carrots	5.1
Milk	6.6
Beer	4.5
Wine	2.9

17 Why do you think the acidity of coloured foods must be measured with a pH meter?

Neutralisation

Acids and alkalis are chemical opposites. When they are mixed they react. The reaction is irreversible and a new substance is formed.

Acids have a pH of less than 7 and alkalis have a pH of greater than 7. When they are mixed the pH moves towards 7. This can be seen using a pH meter. If the pH meter probe is placed in vinegar, the reading is pH 3. If the probe is rinsed and placed in ammonia solution, the reading is pH 11. Adding the alkali slowly to the acid causes the pH of the solution to rise slowly. At pH 7 we say that the acid and alkali are **neutralised**.

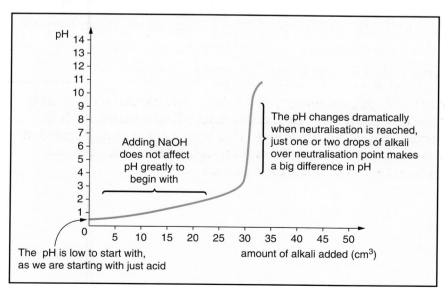

Adding NaOH does not affect pH greatly to begin with

The pH changes dramatically when neutralisation is reached, just one or two drops of alkali over neutralisation point makes a big difference in pH

The pH is low to start with, as we are starting with just acid

7.17 *The change in pH when a strong alkali is added to 25 cm³ of strong acid. This graph was produced using a data logger to monitor the pH change when an acid and alkali are mixed*

18 What will happen to the shape of the graph if we keep adding ammonia to the solution?

Neutralisation in action

Neutralisation is a very important type of reaction. You use it every day of your life. Here are some examples of occasions where we use acids and alkalis to cancel each other out.

Using hair shampoos and conditioners

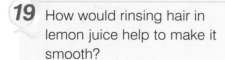

19 How would rinsing hair in lemon juice help to make it smooth?

Shampoos contain a mild alkali to help remove grease. When hair is washed with shampoo the small scales on each hair open out. This makes the hair difficult to comb. It can make the hair stick out once it is dried. Conditioners contain a mild acid. The alkali from the shampoo is neutralised and the scales on the hair shut down. This leaves hair shiny and easier to comb. Many modern hair treatments claim to balance the pH of hair. Some old beauty remedies suggest rinsing hair with lemon juice or vinegar after shampooing.

Cleaning your teeth

Sugar in food and drink provides the bacteria in your mouth with food. As they feed on the sugar they produce an acid which attacks the protective surface of your teeth and can cause decay. Brushing regularly with toothpaste can help protect your teeth. Toothpaste is a mild alkali and helps to neutralise the acids formed.

7.18 *Antacid tablets*

Indigestion

In our stomachs we have hydrochloric acid. It is very dilute but we need it to help digest our food. Sometimes too much is produced and causes indigestion, which is very painful. If the extra acid is neutralised, the indigestion is cured. Taking a weak alkali such as an indigestion tablet will do this. These are often called antacid tablets.

Insect and plant stings

20 How might you treat a wasp sting?

Ant stings, bee stings and nettle stings all contain methanoic acid. The acid causes irritation and is painful when it gets under the skin. To relieve the pain you need to neutralise the acid from the sting. This can be done by adding a weak alkali to the area. If you are stung by a wasp, however, this treatment won't help at all. Wasp stings contain an alkali.

Soil treatment

Plants are often very sensitive to acidity in the soil in which they grow. A plant may not grow at all or grow badly if the soil has the wrong acidity level for it. Each type of plant grows best in its own particular acidity (pH) level. The table shows the pH conditions preferred by different vegetables.

It is important for farmers and gardeners to know how acidic or alkaline their soil is. They carry out regular checks using indicators in a soil test kit. This helps them to choose the best plants for their soil.

Often farmers and gardeners find that the soil is too acidic to grow healthy plants in. They must treat the soil with an alkali to neutralise the acid. Lime is added to the soil because it is alkaline.

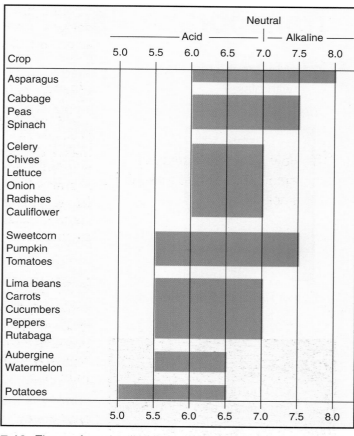

7.19 *The preferred soil pHs for different vegetables*

7.20 *Farmer adding lime to soil*

21 A farmer has soil of pH 5.5. What vegetables would you advise her to grow?

22 Her sister has soil of pH 7. What vegetables would you advise her to grow?

Acid spills

When a strong acid is spilt it must be cleared up quickly. This can happen in the laboratory. It can also happen when a tanker has an accident. The acid can be neutralised by adding an alkali. Once it is neutralised it is no longer corrosive. Usually lime is added to the acid. Another way to treat an acid spill is to dilute it with lots of water. This will help make it less corrosive.

7.21 *Dealing with an acid spill*

TECHNOLOGY BOX

Transporting dangerous chemicals

23 Why are the tankers lined with glass?

7.22 *A Hazchem label from a tanker*

24 Why do you think symbols and numbers are used and not names and instructions?

Many acids and alkalis are used in the chemical industry. They are used to manufacture lots of everyday products. For example, sulphuric acid is used to make paints, fibres and fertilisers. Large amounts of acid and alkali must be transported to and from different factories. Most chemicals are transported by road in tankers. It is important to make sure that nothing goes wrong during the journey. The tankers that carry acids are made of stainless steel and lined with glass.

If an accident occurs it is important that the chemical companies provide accurate information to the emergency services about how to deal with any spillage. One way they do this is to mark the vehicle clearly with a sign.

By law all vehicles carrying hazardous chemicals must carry a sign. This sign must be clearly displayed on the vehicle. Using a code, called the Hazchem Emergency Action Code, the sign provides vital information. This tells the emergency services how to deal with a spillage, leak or fire.

The diamond indicates what the main hazard is. The four-digit number is the United Nations' identification number. This tells the emergency services the name of the chemical in the vehicle. At the bottom of the sign is a telephone number that can be called by the emergency services for expert information.

Cracking the Hazchem code

2P
1830 Sulphuric Acid
CORROSIVE
SPECIALIST ADVICE Teesside (0099) 12345
Haz-Chem Ltd.

7.23 *The Hazchem sign for sulphuric acid*

This example shows the code for sulphuric acid. The numbers and letters in the top left-hand corner of the sign have a particular meaning.

- The number tells the fire brigade what to use to extinguish a fire or deal with a spillage. The number 2 means they must use a fine spray of water.

- The letter P is in the top half of the table. This means that the fire brigade should wash it away (dilute it).

- P also tells them to use breathing apparatus and chemical protective clothing (CPC) when dealing with the spill.

Find out more about transporting acids and alkalis at ▶
www.scienceweb.co.uk

Questions

1 Food and drinks are often stored in metal cans. Some foods have a very low pH value and this can make it difficult to store these foods. In the mid-1800s there were a number of experiments for storing food in metal cans. These cans were made from steel, an iron-based material. It was found that beef kept well but cans containing fruit began to bulge. When these cans were opened a gas was released.

   a What are foods that have a low pH called?

   b How could the gas have formed in the metal can?

2 Tick the correct descriptions of an acid.

   a Acids always burn things.

   b Acids can be corrosive.

   c Acids turn universal indicator blue.

   d Acids turn universal indicator red.

   e Acids neutralise salts.

   f Acids neutralise alkalis.

   g Acids are always poisonous.

   h Acids taste sour.

   i Acids have a high pH.

   j Acids have a low pH.

3 Acids are solutions that can be corrosive to human skin if too strong but they can also be useful. Give an example of the usefulness of the corrosive nature of an acid.

4 Below is a scale for pH.

   a Label the appropriate portions with A = alkali, B = acid and C = neutral.

   c Under the appropriate pH put cola, which is acidic, and soaps, which are alkaline.

   c Name two things you could use to show the pH of a substance.

   d What colour would you see if you tested for an acid with universal indicator?

   e What colour would you see if you tested for an alkali with universal indicator?

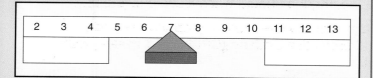

5 Acids and alkali have different pH strengths that indicate if they are weak or strong.

   a What pH does have a weak acid have?

   b What pH does a strong alkali have?

   c If you tested the substances in the following table with a pH meter what pH would you predict?

Substance	pH
Hydrochloric acid	
Washing-up liquid	
Orange juice	
Tap water	
Antacid stomach powder	
Sodium chloride solution	

6 Indigestion is often caused by too much acid in the stomach. The excess acid can be removed by treating with antacid tablets.

   a What type of reaction would take place?

   b The stomach contains hydrochloric acid. What would you expect the pH to be?

   i 2 to 3   **ii** 12 to 13   **iii** 5 to 6   **iv** 8 to 9

   c On the packet of antacid tablets, crunching or dissolving the tablet in the mouth is recommended. Why do you think this is?

   d If you were to investigate this reaction name three variables you could investigate.

   e If you were investigating the speed of the reaction with the size of antacid bits, what variables would you need to keep the same for a fair test?

   f What would you predict about the size of the antacid bits and the speed of the reaction?

   g What would you measure to investigate your prediction?

   h Draw a rough graph to show what you might expect.

7 In Sweden there are many lakes which have little life in them because they are so acidic. Where do you think the acid came from?

8 Complete the following paragraph.
Adding acid to...............changes the............... This can be seen by a change in colour using...............
The chemical reaction is called an...............reaction.
In the reaction the acids...............and...............react to form a new substance. This type of reaction happens when farmers spread lime on the soil, when we clean our teeth and when we treat indigestion.

9 How does pickling food help to stop fruits and vegetables from going off?

10 Raj and Asha want to clean a piece of metal. They know the metal can be cleaned using a strong acid. Which of the following would be a good choice?

   a citric acid pH 4–5   **b** ammonia pH 12–13

   c nitric acid pH 2–3   **d** carbonic acid pH 6

UNIT 8 Simple chemical reactions

Starting points

Many materials can be changed. Some of these changes are reversible. When chocolate is heated it melts to a liquid, but when the melted chocolate cools it becomes solid again. Other changes are irreversible. Once they have happened, it is difficult to get the original materials back again. For example, it is not possible to convert a loaf of bread back into its ingredients.

Sometimes we must heat a mixture of substances to cause a reaction. Air is a mixture of gases. When a substance burns it reacts with the oxygen in the air. The oxygen is one of the reactants.

Learning objectives

Reading this unit will help you to know about and understand the following ideas and processes involved in simple chemical reactions:

That a chemical reaction involves making new substances.

What happens when an acid reacts with a metal.

That some metals do not react with acids and some react strongly.

What happens when an acid reacts with a carbonate.

How to tell if a gas is hydrogen or carbon dioxide.

That when substances burn they react with oxygen in the air and an oxide is made.

About how much oxygen there is in the air around us.

How to use word equations to represent reactions.

Key words

acid	fossil fuel	methane	reactants
carbonate	fuel	oxide	reactive
carbon dioxide	hydrochloric acid	oxygen	reversible change
chemical reaction	hydrogen	particle	salt
combustion	irreversible change	phlogiston	sulphuric acid
flammable		products	word equation
		react	

This mind map summarises the key learning points in this unit.

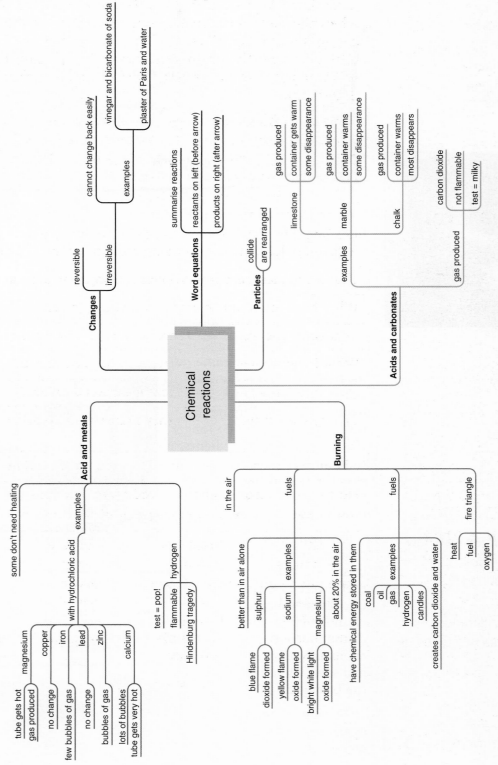

Use mind maps to summarise other units.

Cooking changes

75 g self-raising flour
$\frac{1}{2}$ level tsp of salt
75 g butter
50 g bitter chocolate
2 large eggs
150 g caster sugar
$\frac{1}{2}$ tsp vanilla essence

It was Tom's mother's birthday and he decided to make chocolate brownies for a treat. He found a recipe and collected the ingredients.

The recipe book gave a list of instructions to make the brownies.

> Heat the oven to 170°C.
>
> Grease a shallow baking tin.
>
> Boil a pan of water; place the butter and chocolate in a basin and stand over the water to melt.
>
> Break the eggs into a bowl, add the sugar and vanilla essence and mix well; gradually beat in the chocolate mixture.
>
> Using a tablespoon, stir the flour into the egg mixture.
>
> Pour into the prepared tin and bake in the centre of the oven for 35 minutes. Cool in the tin and then cut into portions.

As he followed the recipe, Tom noticed changes taking place in the ingredients he was using.

The water boiled when it was heated and some of it turned to steam.

The chocolate and butter melted, and became liquids which mixed together.

When the eggs and flour were added to the liquid mixture it became more solid.

When the mixture came out of the oven it had changed again. It was now different from the ingredients he had put in and he could no longer see the separate ingredients in the mixture. Tom knew that the heat from the oven had caused this big change, but did not know how.

Tom had been studying changes in science lessons in school he knew that there were two types of change, **reversible changes** and **irreversible changes**. He thought about the changes he had seen while baking the brownies.

His elder sister, Jenny, explained what had happened.

When different substances are mixed together and then heated in the oven, a chemical reaction happens betweeen the different bits in the mixture. The bits combine together to make a new substance.

1. Sort the changes Tom saw into reversible and irreversible changes.

2. What is the difference between these two types of change?

3. Why do you think the mixture changes when it is heated in the oven?

Jenny was right that a chemical reaction caused the changes in the brownie mixture. But substances do not always have to be heated to cause a reaction. Some substances will react even if they are not heated.

- Vinegar and bicarbonate of soda fizz when they mix. The container they are in becomes warm. The fizz is a gas being produced.

- When plaster of Paris powder and water are mixed they form a paste. This paste hardens into a new material and is used to set broken bones.

Each of these reactions is irreversible. The new substance cannot be easily changed back to the original materials. We say that a chemical reaction has taken place.

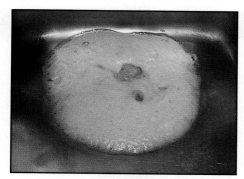

8.1 *The reaction between vinegar and bicarbonate of soda*

4 What evidence might you use to spot a chemical reaction?

Acids and metals

Acids react with some metals without needing to be heated. Acids are corrosive solutions. This means that acids can 'eat' away at some metals.

When they **react**, the acid and the metal make new substances. We cannot change them back into the original materials again. A chemical reaction has taken place.

Tom investigated this reaction in the laboratory by adding small pieces of magnesium to **hydrochloric acid** (HCl) to see what happened. He noticed that a gas was given off. After a few minutes, the magnesium had disappeared. When he touched the test tube he noticed it was quite hot even though he had not heated it.

Not all metals react with hydrochloric acid as easily as magnesium.

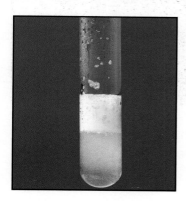

8.2 *The reaction between HCl and magnesium in a test tube*

Metal	Reaction with dilute hydrochloric acid
Copper	No change is seen. No bubbles of gas.
Iron	A few bubbles of gas are seen.
Lead	No change is seen. No bubbles of gas.
Magnesium	The metal disappears quickly. Lots of bubbles are seen and the test tube becomes quite warm.
Zinc	Quite a few bubbles of gas.
Calcium	Metal disappears almost immediately. Lots and lots of bubbles. The test tube becomes very hot.

If these reactions are repeated with other laboratory acids the results are the same.

5 What evidence is there that a chemical reaction has happened?

6 Which metals in the table react with hydrochloric acid? Explain your answer.

7 Which metal reacted most vigorously with HCl? Which was the least **reactive**? Put them in descending order, from most to least reactive.

Hydrogen

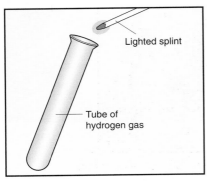

8.3 *Testing for hydrogen*

We can test the gas that comes from the acid and metal reaction. The gas is **hydrogen**. It is a colourless gas that is lighter than air. The picture on the left shows how to test for hydrogen.

The 'pop' is a mini-explosion. This happens when oxygen in the air is ignited with hydrogen. Hydrogen is said to be a **flammable** gas. The hydrogen and oxygen undergo a chemical reaction. Never collect too much hydrogen to test. The more hydrogen you collect the bigger the 'pop' when it reacts with the oxygen in the air. Figure 8.4 shows how to collect enough gas from a reaction to test safely.

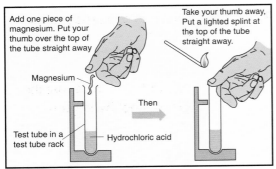

8.4 *Collecting hydrogen*

Tragic end to promising invention

In the 1930s giant balloons full of hydrogen were used to transport goods and people quickly. They were called airships. Hydrogen was used to fill them because it was a very low-density gas and floated well in the air. An airship could carry up to 60 passengers. Before jet aircraft were invented, people thought that airships would be the future of air transport.

However in 1937 an airship called the Hindenburg caught fire and there was a terrible explosion. Many people lost their lives. Nowadays large airships are still used but they are filled with helium instead of hydrogen.

8.5 *Hindenburg in flames*

8 Why was a low-density gas needed to fill airships?

9 Explain what happened to the Hindenburg. What chemical reaction took place?

10 Why do we now fill air balloons with helium and not hydrogen?

11 Draw a cartoon to show how acids particles react with a metal.

12 Why can we not see the salt made in the reaction?

In the reaction with metals, acid particles attack the metal particles. Two new substances are made. They are hydrogen and a new substance called a **salt**, which is dissolved in a solution with water. We can show this using a **word equation**. Word equations are shorthand ways of explaining what is happening in a chemical reaction. Instead of writing out a sentence to explain what has happened we can write a word equation. For example:

acid + metal → salt + hydrogen + energy change

The original substances in the reaction are called the **reactants**. The new substances that are made are the **products** of the reaction.

Acids and carbonate

Acids can also attack stone. Many old statues and monuments are made of stone and are damaged by acid rain. The acid eats away the surface of the stone.

Substance	Reaction with hydrochloric acid
Limestone	Bubbles of gas produced. Container becomes warm. Some of the limestone disappears.
Marble	Bubbles of gas produced. Container becomes warm. A little of the marble disappears.
Chalk	Bubbles of gas produced. Container becomes warm. Most of the chalk disappears.

Marble, chalk and limestone all have one thing in common. They contain a substance called **calcium carbonate**. Tom investigated the effect of hydrochloric acid on these substances in the laboratory. He recorded his observations.

He noticed that a gas was made in each reaction and wondered what it was. He tested to see if it was hydrogen but it wasn't.

Carbon dioxide

The gas made when acids react with calcium carbonate is called **carbon dioxide**.

Carbon dioxide is a colourless gas but it is not flammable like hydrogen. It is used in fire extinguishers as it is more dense (heavier) than air. This means it can form a blanket over the fire and prevent air from reaching the fire. It is also put into drinks to make them fizzy.

Tom mixed some other substances with hydrochloric acid. They reacted just like the calcium carbonate.

Substance	Reaction with hydrochloric acid
Washing soda	Bubbles of carbon dioxide produced. Container becomes warm. The washing soda rapidly disappears.
Baking powder	Bubbles of carbon dioxide produced. Container becomes warm. The baking powder rapidly disappears.

Washing soda and baking powder are carbonates, just like marble and chalk. All carbonates make carbon dioxide when acid is added to them. Another substance is made too. This is called a salt and it is dissolved in the mixture. We can show the reaction using a word equation.

acid + carbonate → salt + water + carbon dioxide + energy change

8.6 *The effects of acid rain on a gargoyle*

13 What has happened to this statue?

14 How did Tom know that the gas was not hydrogen?

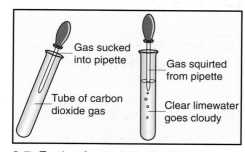

Gas sucked into pipette

Gas squirted from pipette

Tube of carbon dioxide gas

Clear limewater goes cloudy

8.7 *Testing for carbon dioxide*

15 How are hydrogen and carbon dioxide similar? How are they different?

16 How do we know an energy change has happened?

17 When marble and hydrochloric acid react to produce carbon dioxide, what are the reactants and what is the product?

Heating and burning

When substances burn in oxygen they burn much more vigorously than they do in air. For example, when sodium burns in air it burns with a bright, white light. When it burns in **oxygen** it burns even more brightly. It forms a white powder called sodium oxide. When sodium oxide is dissolved in water, it makes an alkaline solution. This solution turns universal indicator blue.

When sulphur burns in air it burns with a small blue flame. When it burns in oxygen the blue flame is bigger and brighter. It forms a gas called sulphur dioxide. Sulphur dioxide gas turns universal indicator red.

8.8 *Burning sodium in air and in oxygen*

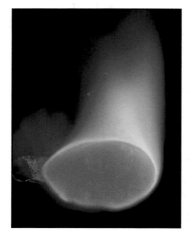

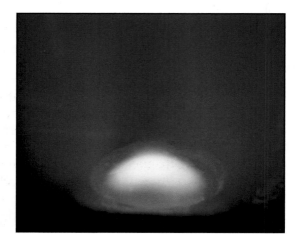

8.9 *Burning sulphur in air and in oxygen*

When these substances burn a chemical reaction takes place and a new substance is made. The original substance combines with the oxygen and makes a new substance. The product is an **oxide**.

- Sulphur combines with oxygen to make sulphur dioxide.
- Sodium combines with oxygen to make sodium oxide.

sulphur + oxygen → sulphur dioxide + energy change

sodium + oxygen → sodium oxide + energy change

The reaction that takes place when a substance burns is called **combustion**. The product of combustion is always an **oxide.**

18 What are the reactants and the products in these reactions?

19 Write a word equation for the burning of magnesium in oxygen.

Chemical reactions and particles

All materials are made up of particles. When a chemical reaction takes place the particles in the reactants are rearranged into new patterns. For example, if 50 g of sulphur are burned until there are 25 g of sulphur left, where do the other 25 g of sulphur go?

Particles cannot be destroyed by a chemical reaction. This means the missing sulphur particles must have gone somewhere else. Before the experiment the sulphur particles were arranged in a regular pattern, close together. As the sulphur burned, some of the sulphur particles joined up with the oxygen particles in the air. This made sulphur dioxide. As sulphur dioxide is a gas it spread through the air. If all the sulphur dioxide could be collected it would contain 25 g of sulphur particles.

Burning magnesium

Magnesium ribbon burns with a brilliant white flame. When magnesium is burned in a crucible, the contents are found to weigh more at the end of the reaction than they did at the beginning. This is because burning magnesium joins up with oxygen in the air. The extra mass is the mass of the oxygen particles that are added to the magnesium particles.

Using the figures in the diagram we can find out what percentage (%) of the magnesium oxide is oxygen.

$$\frac{\text{Mass of oxygen present}}{\text{Total mass of magnesium oxide}} \times 100 = \%$$

Mass of oxygen in magnesium oxide = total mass of magnesium oxide – mass of magnesium

$$= 4.0 \text{ g} - 2.4 \text{ g}$$
$$= 1.6 \text{ g}$$

So the percentage of magnesium oxide which is made from oxygen particles is:

$$\frac{1.6}{4.0} \times 100 = 40\%$$

If we weighed all the reactants at the beginning of the reaction and all the products at the end, we would find that the mass before the reaction mass is the same as the mass after the reaction. All the gases involved must also be weighed. This is because when there is a chemical reaction the mass of reactants = the mass of products.

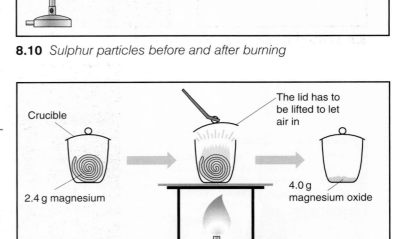

8.10 *Sulphur particles before and after burning*

8.11 *Before, during and after the burning of magnesium*

20 3.0 g of sodium oxide are formed when 1.5 g of sodium are burned in air. What percentage of sodium oxide is oxygen?

HISTORY BOX
How to explain burning

21 Write an explanation for each of these observations.

When scientists try to understand how and why something happens they use evidence. They need to consider all the evidence and then come up with a theory or model to explain what is happening.

In the 17th century scientists were having problems explaining burning. They needed to come up with a theory that fitted all the evidence they had. This is what they knew.

- When fuels are burned they lose mass. For example, the ashes left after burning wood have less mass than the original piece of wood.
- Some fuels leave virtually nothing behind when they burn.
- A flame goes out when burned in an enclosed space.
- A mouse dies in an airtight space.

Scientists thought that all materials that burned contained a substance called **phlogiston**. When a material burned the phlogiston was released into the air. The air could absorb phlogiston.

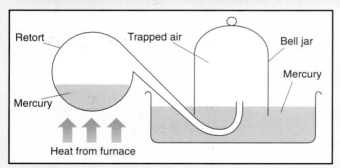

Some things lose mass when they burn because they lose phlogiston

The flame goes out in an enclosed space because the air becomes full of phlogiston

A mouse dies in an airtight space because the air becomes full of phlogiston

Some fuels are nearly all phlogiston and so leave very little behind when they burn

This phlogiston theory could explain all the evidence above.

However, scientists ignored one piece of evidence. *When metals burned in air they gained mass.* Many did not have the scientific equipment to be able to measure the very small increases in mass that occurred. Others said that the experiments that did show an increase in mass must have been inaccurate.

A French scientist called Antoine Lavoisier came up with another theory. He proved that when a material burns it gains mass if all the products are collected. This increase in mass is due to the material gaining oxygen. Because the increase in mass is so small, Lavoisier had to be able to measure mass very accurately. He also needed to collect any gases produced in burning. He did this by collecting any gases produced over mercury or water.

Retort
Trapped air
Bell jar
Mercury
Mercury
Heat from furnace

8.12 *Lavoisier's equipment*

This required a lot of skill. His careful work disproved the phlogiston theory. It established the combustion theory that we use today.

22 Why was it easier for Lavoisier to measure the change in the mass of a burning metal rather than burning wood?

Fuels

All materials have chemical energy stored inside them. Burning materials releases this energy as heat and light. Sometimes the energy released is only very small. Sometimes it is very large. If very large amounts of energy are released all at once an explosion happens.

Some materials release lots of energy very steadily. These materials are very useful to us as we can use them as **fuels**. Most of the energy used to cook food, drive cars and keep us warm comes from coal, oil and gas. These materials release plenty of heat energy when they burn and they burn steadily.

Coal, oil and natural gas are **fossil fuels.** This means that they are the remains of plants and animals that lived millions of years ago. Other fuels that we use for heat and light include wax candles, petrol, paraffin, propane (camping gas) and butane (lighter fuel). All these fuels are made from fossil fuels.

8.13 *Too much energy released all at once causes an explosion*

Products of burning

Many people use natural gas to cook with or to heat their homes. The chemical name for natural gas is **methane**. When methane burns it releases energy in the form of heat and light. As burning is a chemical reaction, new substances or products are formed. The burners used in science laboratories also burn natural gas.

The products of burning methane are carbon dioxide and water. This means that methane must be made up of carbon and hydrogen. The carbon is oxidised to carbon dioxide. The hydrogen is oxidised to hydrogen oxide (water).

We can show this reaction using a word equation:

methane + oxygen → carbon dioxide + water + energy change

If this investigation is repeated using a wax candle, petrol or a piece of wood the results are the same. This shows that fossil fuels are made up of mainly carbon and hydrogen. When any fossil fuel burns the products of burning are carbon dioxide and water. This means that there is a general word equation to describe how fossil fuels burn:

fossil fuel + oxygen → carbon dioxide + water + energy change

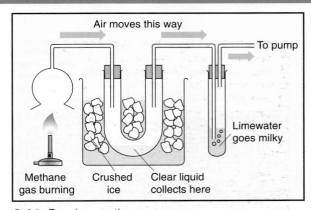

8.14 *Burning methane gas*

23 Where does carbon dioxide come from?

24 What are the reactants and what are the products in this reaction?

25 Draw a diagram to show how the oxygen particles from the air react with carbon and hydrogen particles in the fuel.

Putting out fires

To make a fire, three things are needed. This is shown on the fire triangle. It has three sides, heat, fuel and air (or oxygen). If one of these is missing there will be no fire. To stop a fire one side of the triangle must be removed. This will put out the fire.

8.15 *The fire triangle*

To put out a bonfire you should hose it down with water. This cools down the fire and the heat is removed from the triangle.

If someone's clothes catch fire you should roll them in a blanket or curtain. This cuts off the air supply. The air is removed from the triangle.

To stop a forest fire from spreading, fire fighters cut down some of the trees. This takes away the fire's fuel. The fuel is removed from the triangle.

WARNING
Petrol fires, electrical fires or chip pan fires should never be hosed down with water.

26 When a fire starts in one part of a house it is important to close all the windows and doors to stop draughts. Explain why.

27 Draw a flow chart to explain what happens when a candle burns.

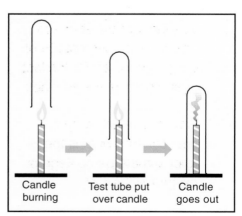

8.17 *The effects of limited oxygen on a burning candle*

Candle burning → Test tube put over candle → Candle goes out

Burning a wax candle

When a candle burns, heat is released. Lighting the wick produces enough heat to melt the wax at the top of the candle. The melted wax then evaporates and this gas is the fuel that ignites and burns. The energy from this burning reaction provides the heat to keep melting and evaporating the wax. This provides a constant supply of fuel to keep burning.

However, if a container is placed over the candle and the supply of air is cut off the candle goes out. If a larger container is placed over the candle, it will continue to burn for a little longer. This is because there is more oxygen available for burning. It is possible to investigate what happens if different-sized containers are placed over a burning candle.

The investigation is carried out using different-sized containers and timing how long it takes for a candle to go out.

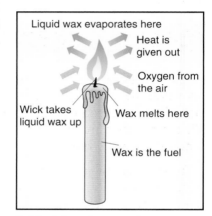

Liquid wax evaporates here
Heat is given out
Oxygen from the air
Wick takes liquid wax up
Wax melts here
Wax is the fuel

8.16 *A burning candle*

Size of container (cm³)	Time taken for candle to go out (seconds)
100	2.5
250	10
400	15
500	20
750	27.5
1000	30

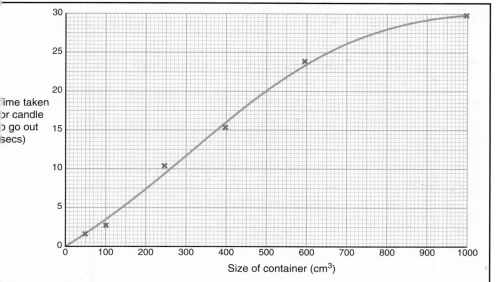

The results have been plotted on the graph on the left.

28 Explain what the shape of the graph shows.

8.18 How long a candle can burn in beakers containing different volumes of air

How much oxygen is there in the air?

The investigation can be repeated, this time with the candle floating on water, to measure how much oxygen there is in the air. When the container is placed over the burning candle the level of the water rises. This is because the water rises to take the place of the oxygen used up when the candle burns.

To find out the amount of oxygen in the air, a container was placed over the top of a floating candle. The water level was marked on the container. Once the candle had gone out the new water level was marked. The amount of oxygen used could then be worked out.

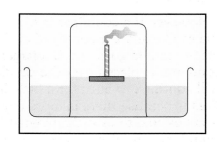

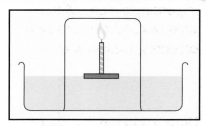

$$\frac{\text{Amount of oxygen used}}{\text{Total volume of air in the container}} \times 100 = \text{\% oxygen in air}$$

29 Can you think why this enquiry is difficult to do?

30 Use the formula above to calculate the percentage of oxygen in the air for the last three containers in the table.

31 From the results in the final column, what is the approximate percentage of oxygen in the air?

32 Getting reliable results from this investigation is not easy. Explain why.

33 Which results do not seem to fit the pattern? What could be done about this?

Volume of the measuring cylinder used (cm^3)	Amount of oxygen used up in burning (cm^3)	% of oxygen in the air
100	17	$\frac{17}{100} \times 100 = 17\%$
250	48	$\frac{48}{250} \times 100 = 19.2\%$
400	100	$\frac{100}{400} \times 100 = 25\%$
500	100	
750	140	
1000	198	

TECHNOLOGY BOX

Making an acid

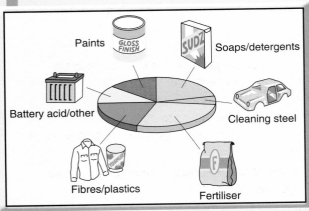

8.19 *Different uses of sulphuric acid*

Sulphuric acid is a very important chemical in industry. It is used to make many different products that we use every day. The pie chart shows some of them.

A lot of sulphuric acid is used in industry. Scientists have found a way to make it cheaply and easily. Yellow sulphur powder is burned in air and sulphur dioxide gas is made. This happens when the sulphur reacts with the oxygen in the air. It is an oxidation reaction. The next step is more difficult. The sulphur dioxide gas must now react with more oxygen. This reaction makes another gas, called sulphur trioxide. The sulphur trioxide is then added to water and sulphuric acid is formed.

The flow diagram below shows each of the processes involved in the manufacture of sulphuric acid.

Here are the different reactions in the process.

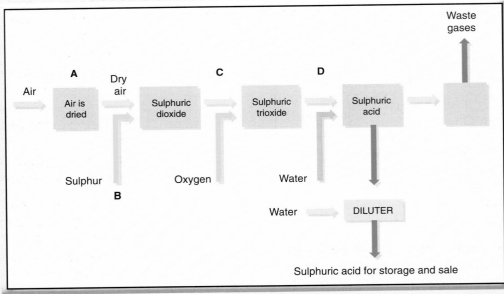

8.20 *The manufacture of sulphuric acid*

34 How many chemical reactions are involved in making sulphuric acid?

35 Write a sentence describing what is happening at A, B, C and D.

Questions

1 Frying an egg makes egg protein change.
  a Is the change a reversible or irreversible change?
  b Is the change a physical or chemical change?
  c Where does the energy come from to cause the change?

2 Metal A reacts with acid very slowly.
  Metal B reacts explosively with acid.
  Metal C reacts very fast with acid.
  a Arrange these metals in order of their decreasing reaction with acid.
  b What gas is released in these reactions?
  c What type of substance is left dissolved in water in the reaction?
  d The gas from metal B's reaction with acid reacted explosively with another substance. What was that other substance?

3 Describe the test for hydrogen gas and write a word equation to describe what happens.

4 Many buildings around us are made from limestone or marble. Sadly many of these buildings are under attack from the rain. The rain in cities has dissolved substances which attack the rock.
  a What chemical is found in limestone and marble?
  b What substances does rain dissolve?
  c What could be the pH of the rainwater?
  d Write a word equation for the chemical reaction between rainwater and limestone.
  e What gas is released when rainwater reacts with limestone?
  f What other rock is made from the same chemical as limestone and marble?

5 Making cakes and breads often requires the use of a raising agent. These are substances which react with acids or release a gas when heated. One of these substances is baking powder.
  a What gas is released when baking powder is heated?
  b What type of compound is baking powder?
  c What would you see if you put some baking powder in a test tube and added acid to it?
  d Give one other use of the gas that is released.

6 Complete these chemical equations.
  a carbon + oxygen → ....
  b .... + ... → magnesium oxide
  c sulphur + ... → sulphur oxide

7 When things burn they require three things to be present. One of these is heat.
  a What are the two other things?
  b What is burning with flames called?
  c Why does a fire go out when carbon dioxide is put on it?
  d What do we call a substance that releases heat energy very quickly?
  e Give two examples of such a substance.

8 When magnesium burns it reacts very violently with a bright white light and high temperature to a substance in the air.
  a What is this substance?
  b The atmosphere consists of the following gases:
      Nitrogen   79%
      Oxygen   20%
      Other gases   1%
  Draw a pie chart showing the proportions of gases in the atmosphere.
  c If the magnesium was burned in a container with a volume of 50 cm³, what volume of the air would be used up?
  d Write a word equation for the reaction between magnesium and oxygen.

9 Raj put some magnesium into hydrochloric acid. He took the temperature of the acid before and after he added the magnesium.
  a What would Raj see happening in the test tube?
  b What is released from the reaction?
  c What would you predict would happen to the temperature and why?
  d Write a word equation for the reaction.
  e What would Raj see if he put copper in the acid instead of magnesium?

UNIT 9 Energy resources

Starting points

When some substances are burned they give out heat and light. These substances are called fuels, and we use them to provide energy for heating and cooking.

Living things need energy too. Animals eat food which helps them to grow, and provides energy to keep them alive. Plants make their own food using energy from sunlight.

Learning objectives

Reading this unit will help you to know about and understand the ideas and processes to do with energy resources:

That fuels are substances which burn to release energy.

That coal, mineral oil and gas are examples of fossil fuels which are non-renewable sources of energy.

About how fossil fuels were made.

That renewable sources of energy include wind, waves, running water, sunlight, biomass and geothermal energy.

About some of the problems caused by using fossil fuels.

About the advantages of renewable energy resources.

That energy is measured in Joules.

That food is the energy source of animals.

That sunlight is the energy source of green plants.

That the Sun is the source of almost all of the Earth's energy resources.

Key words

acid rain	fossilised	hydroelectric	renewable
biomass	fuel	Joules	respiration
carbohydrate	fuel cell	natural gas	solar
coal	geothermal	non-renewable	solar cell
crude oil	global warming	oil	tidal barrage
diesel	greenhouse effect	photosynthesis	wind farm
energy		pollution	
fossil fuel			

Learning methods ▼

These flash cards summarise the key learning points in this unit.

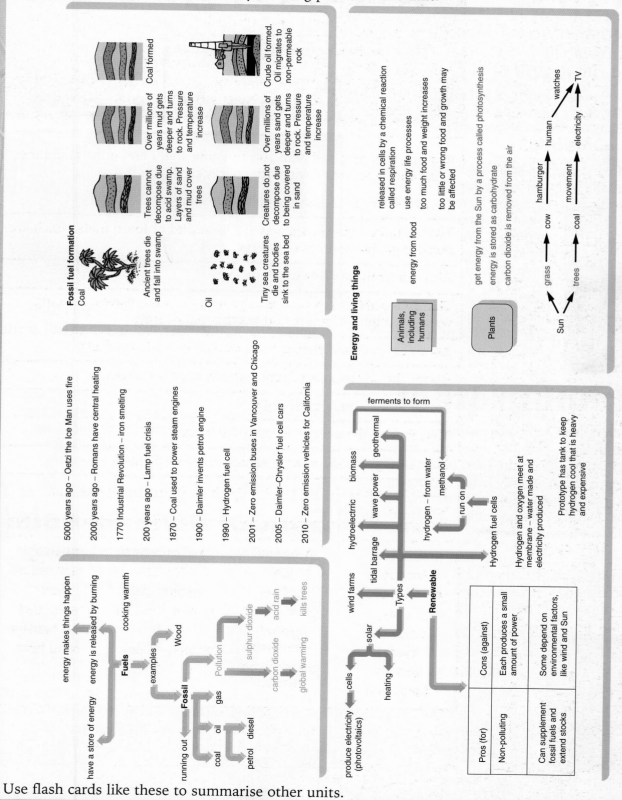

Fossil fuel formation

Coal

- Ancient trees die and fall into swamp
- Trees cannot decompose due to acid swamp. Layers of sand and mud cover trees
- Over millions of years mud gets deeper and turns to rock. Pressure and temperature increase
- Coal formed

Oil

- Tiny sea creatures die and bodies sink to the sea bed
- Creatures do not decompose due to being covered in sand
- Over millions of years sand gets deeper and turns to rock. Pressure and temperature increase
- Crude oil formed. Oil migrates to non-permeable rock

Energy and living things

Animals, including humans
- energy from food
  - released in cells by a chemical reaction called respiration
  - use energy life processes
  - too much food and weight increases
  - too little or wrong food and growth may be affected

Plants
- get energy from the Sun by a process called photosynthesis
- energy is stored as carbohydrate
- carbon dioxide is removed from the air

- grass → cow → hamburger → human → watches
- trees → coal → movement → electricity → TV
- Sun → grass
- Sun → trees

- 5000 years ago – Oetzi the Ice Man uses fire
- 2000 years ago – Romans have central heating
- 1770 Industrial Revolution – iron smelting
- 200 years ago – Lamp fuel crisis
- 1870 – Coal used to power steam engines
- 1900 – Daimler invents petrol engine
- 1990 – Hydrogen fuel cell
- 2001 – Zero emission buses in Vancouver and Chicago
- 2005 – Daimler–Chrysler fuel cell cars
- 2010 – Zero emission vehicles for California

Renewable
- Types
  - geothermal
  - biomass → ferments to form → methanol → run on → Hydrogen fuel cells
  - wave power
  - hydroelectric
  - tidal barrage
  - hydrogen – from water
  - wind farms
  - solar
    - cells → produce electricity (photovoltaics)
    - heating
- Hydrogen fuel cells
  - Hydrogen and oxygen meet at membrane – water made and electricity produced
  - Prototype has tank to keep hydrogen cool that is heavy and expensive

Pros (for)	Cons (against)
Non-polluting	Each produces a small amount of power
Can supplement fossil fuels and extend stocks	Some depend on environmental factors, like wind and Sun

Fuels
- energy makes things happen
- have a store of energy
- energy is released by burning
  - cooking warmth
- examples
  - Wood
  - Fossil
    - coal
    - oil
    - gas
      - petrol
      - diesel
- running out
- Pollution
  - sulphur dioxide → acid rain → kills trees
  - carbon dioxide → global warming

Use flash cards like these to summarise other units.

Printed on recycled paper

Energy Echo

1st April 2050

Oil is running out!

The Government today announced that the last oil rig had stopped pumping oil and gas from the North Sea. The Energy Minister told waiting reporters that the oil field had run dry.

The immediate effects of this will be that power stations will no longer produce enough electricity to meet our needs. The cost of petrol will rise dramatically from Monday.

When asked what the Government would do to ease the crises, the Minister suggested: "Our only hope now is to move to the use of renewable energy resources. We intend to invest in this area heavily."

1 Why might our supply of oil run out?

Windmill protest

Local protesters have wrecked a windmill in a small town in Yorkshire. The windmill was part of a new wind farm built on the local hillside. It aimed to produce 'clean' energy using the power of the wind. "I can't understand it," said the owner of the wind farm, "we are creating a clean environment with less pollution here."

Protestors disagreed. "We don't want these ugly great monstrosities next to our village," their spokesman protested. "There was never any pollution here anyway. That's all in the cities."

2 Would you like to live near to a wind farm?

3 What is meant by 'global warming'?

Flood alert

Yet again South West England has been hit by floods. Thousands have had to leave their homes as rivers burst their banks. Five nights of heavy rain have been more than the flood defences could take. Local residents have had to suffer flooding four times in the last 6 years. Many say they will have to leave the area for good. Scientists at the local weather centre are blaming the floods on global warming. "We are paying the price for overuse of cheap fuel during the last century," a spokeswoman said.

School bans sweets!

A secondary school in Newcastle has banned pupils from eating sweets on the school premises. Those who are caught in possession of sweets risk a week's exclusion.

This dramatic step was ordered after a meeting of the school governors. Their chairman explained, "We believe that sweets give children too much energy. The more they eat, the more they run around and get excited." She added that the school hoped that reducing the pupils' sweet intake would help to make for a calmer atmosphere in lessons.

Fuels and energy

Modern life depends on a constant supply of energy. Energy warms our homes, powers our cars and other machines, lights our streets, and much, much more. Life would not be the same without it.

A **fuel** is a substance which contains a store of energy. We burn fuels to release the **energy** stored in it. When a fuel burns, it gives out heat and light. We use energy from fuels in many ways.

Without fuels we would have no lighting, no heating, no motorised transport and no way of cooking food.

Some people use **wood** as a fuel. They burn it to provide heat for warming their homes and cooking.

Petrol and **diesel** are the fuels we burn in motor vehicle engines.

Coal, **gas** and **oil** are fuels burnt in our homes for central heating, cooking or in an open fire place. They are also burnt in power stations to generate electricity.

9.1 *Burning fuel gives out heat and light*

9.2 *Different fuels and their uses*

4 Which fuels are used in your home?

HISTORY BOX
Fuels in history

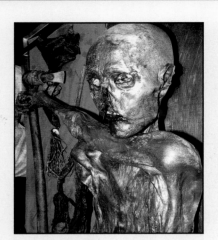

9.3 *Oetzi, the Ice Man*

5 Why did the Ice Man carry burning embers with him?

6 What fuels do you think the Romans used? Give a reason for your answer.

Our first fuel was wood. When people first discovered fire they could have light and heat at night. They could also cook the meat of the animals they hunted. This meant that they could eat more of the meat more easily. It was by using fire that prehistoric people made hard-wearing clay pots and discovered how to use metal.

In 1998 Oetzi the Ice Man was found, frozen, high in the Alps between Italy and Austria. He lived 5000 years ago and in his bag he carried glowing embers from his last fire to make fire-lighting easier and help him survive on the mountain.

Three thousand years after Oetzi the Romans developed a way to warm their houses in cooler climates. They used underground central heating – hypocausts. Archaeologists still find remains of Roman villas with hypocausts under elaborate mosaic floors.

9.4 *A Roman underground heating system*

Two hundred years ago there was an energy crisis. At that time people used whale oil to burn in oil lamps. Whale oil was made from the bodies of whales which had been hunted and the sperm whale population was being hunted to extinction. People were worried that once the last sperm whale was dead they would have no oil for their lamps.

In the end their problem was solved. A new lamp was invented which burnt mineral oil.

The Industrial Revolution began in Britain in the 1770s when Abraham Derby discovered how to use coke (made from coal) to smelt large quantities of iron. From now on engineers would have as much steel as they needed to build huge steam engines for railways and factories. Life for everyone changed more in the following 200 years than it had done in the previous 2000.

7 What changes do you think the industrial revolution made in people's daily lives?

9.5 *The iron bridge at Ironbridge, Shropshire*

Fossil fuels

Coal, mineral oil and gas have to be dug out from underground (or underwater) deposits. There are coal mines, oil wells and gas wells around the world. These fuels are called **fossil fuels**. The same processes that made fossils out of the bodies of early living things formed these fuels.

Coal is made from **fossilised** trees. Millions of years ago the trees died, fell to the ground and were buried in swamps. The trees did not rot in the swamps because the water was acidic. The organisms that rot dead things could not live in it. As time went by layers of mud and sand covered them. Over millions of years the layers of mud slowly turned to rock. Beneath the rock, pressure built up. Chemical reactions gave off heat. Slowly the pressure and heat turned the wood into coal.

Oil was also formed millions of years ago. It is made from the bodies of tiny sea creatures and plants. When they died their soft bodies sank to the bottom of the sea.

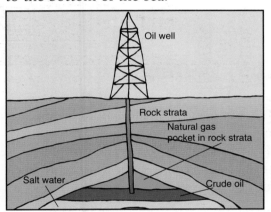

The bodies did not rot away. Over many years, they were buried under layers of sand. Under the great weight of sand deposits, rocks were formed. High pressure and high temperatures developed. The remains slowly changed into the thick, dark liquid we now call **crude oil**.

Once the crude oil was formed it seeped up through the layers of rock until it became trapped by an impermeable dome of rock. Gas formed at the same time, and collected in pockets in this rock.

Crude oil is particularly useful. It is used to make petrol and diesel for cars and aviation fuel for aircraft. It can be burnt to heat the water in a central heating system. It is used in power stations to make electricity. Plastic, medicines and even bitumen for making road surfaces all come from crude oil. So it is easy to see why crude oil is running out quickly.

No one knows for sure how much coal and oil there is left underground so oil companies are racing to find the last few deposits. This is why oil and other fossil fuels are called **non-renewable** resources. Once we have used it all, it is gone forever. Imagine what your life would be like without these fuels – no petrol or oil driven transport, no gas for cooking, no electricity made from coal, oil and gas, no home heating, no computer games!

We can all help to prevent an energy crisis. Turning off lights, turning down the central heating and insulating our houses will save money and use less energy.

8 Why are coal and oil called fossil fuels?

9.6 *Coal*

9 Crude oil is sometimes called 'liquid gold'. Why do you think this is?

10 Why can't we make more coal and oil?

11 What would be the worst effect on *your* life if fossil fuels ran out?

Problems with pollution

There's another reason to think twice before we burn oil – **pollution**. Like the other fossil fuels, when we burn oil, it gives out a gas called carbon dioxide. Carbon dioxide is what we breathe out naturally when we exhale. But burning fossil fuels produces huge amounts of carbon dioxide. It rises into the atmosphere and acts like a blanket around the Earth. It stops heat leaving the planet's surface.

This is called the **greenhouse effect**. The Earth is slowly getting warmer and warmer. Some scientists believe that this **global warming** will change our weather, making the polar ice caps melt and creating new desert areas as well. This would make it far more difficult for things to live on the Earth.

9.7 *Melting polar ice*

Is the world really getting warmer?

Scientists agree that the amount of carbon dioxide in the atmosphere is much higher than it was 200 years ago. Burning coal, for example, releases the carbon dioxide that the trees absorbed when they grew millions of years ago. Scientists also agree that carbon dioxide in the atmosphere can act like a blanket. It traps heat around the Earth and makes the Earth warmer. The Earth is now, on average, 2°C warmer than it was 200 years ago.

Some people are worried that the Earth is getting too warm. They call this global warming. They claim that polar ice caps are melting and that more deserts are forming. They are worried that burning fossil fuels will change the climate, ruin the planet and make it impossible to live here.

Other people point out that the Earth is always changing its climate. There have been several major ice ages when glaciers covered the British Isles. At other times it was warm enough for lions and tigers to live here. We have also had mini ice ages. In the 17th century it was so cold that the river Thames froze over, while in the Middle Ages there was a very warm climate and the average temperature was several degrees higher than it is today.

It is certain that the average temperature of the Earth is rising. What we cannot be certain about is whether this is a problem caused by burning fossil fuels. It may be what is happening to the climate naturally.

9.8 *Extreme desert conditions*

12 What do you think: is the world getting warmer?

Acid rain is another pollution problem caused by burning fossil fuels. The smoke made by burning coal, petrol and diesel contains some unpleasant gases as well as the soot particles which make our clothes and hair dirty. One of these gases – **sulphur dioxide** – rises into the air, mixes with the water in the air and makes **sulphuric acid**. It is the sulphuric acid in rain which causes major problems when rain falls on forests. It harms the leaves and kills the trees.

9.9 *Pine forests damaged by acid rain*

Asthma sufferers know that pollution from traffic makes their problem worse too. Modern cars with catalytic converters produce less pollution than older cars did, but there are so many cars on the road that there is still a serious pollution problem.

9.10 *Using an asthma inhaler*

13 Make a list of pollution problems caused by burning fossil fuels.

Renewable energy resources

Luckily, fossil fuels are not our only source of energy. The Earth is full of many very powerful energy sources that will never run out. The wind, falling water, waves and the Sun are all sources of energy which could be used instead of coal and oil. Because they will never run out, these are called **renewable** energy resources. Scientists are working out new ways of harnessing the energy that is all around us.

14 What does 'renewable energy' mean?

In the United Kingdom and Japan large **wind farms** are being built. Instead of enormous columns of electricity pylons marching across the countryside, we see huge turbines perched on bleak hilltops turning gently in the wind to generate electricity.

In Scotland and Wales waterfalls turn turbines to generate electricity while the Aswan High Dam on the river Nile in Egypt produces electricity as water flows through it. These schemes are called **hydroelectric power generators**.

9.11 *A wind farm*

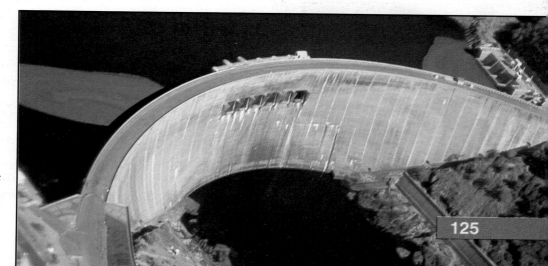

9.12 *Damming for a hydroelectric power station*

15 Where is the best place to build a tidal barrage?

9.13 *The tidal barrage at Rance*

16 Do you think we could use solar power in Britain? Give reasons for your answer.

9.16 *Emergency phones in Australia*

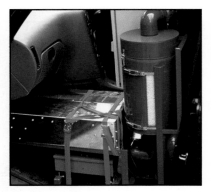

9.17 *A hydrogen fuel cell*

At Rance, in France, a **tidal barrage** produces electricity when the tide rises and falls. The moving water turns a huge waterwheel which is the electricity generator. Other countries are investigating **wave power** as a source of energy.

In Iceland, hot rocks are an alternative source of energy. Water pumped down into the ground comes back as steam. This is called **geothermal** energy.

9.14 *A geothermal power station*

Solar power has been used for a long time in the Mediterranean for heating water – almost every house in Turkey has a large black water tank on the roof to absorb the sun's heat during the day.

9.15 *Solar-heated water tanks*

In Australia's desert the emergency phones are all powered by **solar cells (photovoltaics)** which generate electricity from the Sun's rays. Solar cells also power the hundreds of satellites which orbit the earth to send us TV programmes, monitor the weather or spy on other countries.

Biomass is the name given to plant material that rots and releases energy. This happens naturally in a compost heap so it gets hot. But under the right conditions the bacteria cause the biomass to ferment and produce a fuel called methanol. Methanol is a type of alcohol which can be used in **hydrogen fuel cells** to generate electricity. Electric cars in the 21st century are likely to run on hydrogen fuel cells fed by methanol.

The pros and cons

There is another advantage to renewable energy sources. They do not cause pollution like fossil fuels. Fossil fuels give off soot, poisonous gases and carbon dioxide when we burn them.

The problem with some of the renewable energy sources is that they depend on the weather. The British Isles have a good supply of wind but you cannot rely on it all the time. Some countries do not have enough sunlight to make solar power work. And you cannot use hydroelectric power if there are no waterfalls or large dams in your area.

Also, each sustainable energy installation (wind farm/hydroelectric power station/barrage/dam, etc.) only produces a small amount of energy. This means that, at the moment, all they can do is feed their electricity into the National Grid. They cannot produce enough energy to replace normal power stations.

There is a lot of debate about how to use renewable energy. Some people think that each country should use different renewable sources to supplement their fossil fuel power stations. This way the fossil fuels will last longer.

Other people think that hydrogen fuel cells are the best option as they run on hydrogen or methanol. The fuel cell can be used to run your car or to power your house. Methanol is made from biomass and hydrogen is made from water using the electricity from solar, wind, wave or hydroelectric power. Either way there is plenty of energy and little pollution.

17 Make a list of the *good points* and the *problems* of renewable energy sources.

Pause for thought

- It takes the electricity generated by one full-sized power station just to keep the traffic lights in London going.

- As electricity is sent to out houses along overhead power cables 6–7% of the energy is lost heating up the air around the cable.

- When a driver puts petrol into a car over two-thirds of the petrol will be wasted heating up the engine and making a noise. Only one-third will make the car move. This means that if you put £30 of petrol into the car, £20 of it is wasted.

- Leaving a television on standby costs the same in electricity as leaving it switched on.

- A battery-powered car may not be better for the environment than a conventional car. As you recharge it you use electricity generated in a power station. Burning fossil fuels in a power station still produces pollution.

- A family of four in Britain would need about 50 m^2 solar cells on the roof of the house, pointing south, to provide all the electricity they need.

- Some companies are developing electricity generators which are the size of a washing machine and run on hydrogen. If this proved practical, each house could have its own power station. There would be no more electricity pylons and overhead cables – and no more power cuts.

TECHNOLOGY BOX

Science fiction to fact

I believe that water will one day serve as fuel, that its constituent elements, hydrogen and oxygen, used together or separately, will be an inexhaustible source of heat and light of much greater power than coal possesses. Bunkers, ships and locomotive tenders will store these two condensed gases instead of coal and they will burn in boilers producing enormous heat... I believe that we shall heat our houses and warm ourselves with water after the coal deposits are used up. Water will be the coal of the future.

9.18 *Cyrus Harding, American engineer in Jules Verne's novel* The Mysterious Island *published in 1870*

This prediction was made in 1870 in a science fiction novel. The main source of power in the industrial world at that time was coal. This fuel was used to drive steam engines.

Then, 100 years ago, Gottlieb Daimler put the first internal combustion engine onto a horseless carriage. He invented the motor car. Since then motor transport has relied upon oil as its main fuel. The number of cars on our roads has gone up and up, as they have become cheaper to make. The amount of fuel burnt to drive them has gone up too. And as the number of cars has increased so has the pollution they cause.

Exhaust fumes from vehicles cause over half of the air pollution in our cities. In California the problem is so bad that they have brought in zero-emission laws. These laws insist that by 2010 all cars on the road in California must be electric cars which give out non-polluting exhaust fumes.

9.19 *A 19th century steam-driven vehicle*

18 Why were early cars called horseless carriages?

19 What does 'zero emission' mean?

The first zero-emission cars were powered by batteries. But powerful batteries are large and heavy. They are not very reliable and you cannot travel very far before they need recharging. They were just not good enough to satisfy the needs of drivers. Then, during the early 1990s, a solution to this problem was found. Hydrogen fuel cells, which can provide energy with no pollution, were invented.

9.20 *An early Daimler car*

TECHNOLOGY BOX

A fuel cell is like a battery but it generates electricity using hydrogen and oxygen as fuels. The two gases meet at the central membrane and combine with each other to make pure water and generate electricity.

Many major car manufacturers have now decided to build electric cars that run on hydrogen fuel cells. Daimler–Chrysler plans to be turning out 100,000 engines running on hydrogen fuel cells each year by 2005. These engines will power their Mercedes A class as well as other cars. It is likely that in the 21st century most cars will be driven by hydrogen.

The prototype Necar 4 has its fuel cells under its floor. The liquid-hydrogen fuel is stored in a special low-temperature tank. The oxygen needed comes from the air. These two gases are fed to the fuel cells and a condenser captures waste water. An air-cooled radiator gets rid of waste heat.

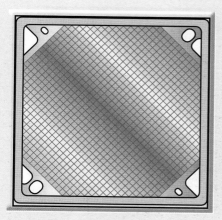

9.21 *Inside a fuel cell*

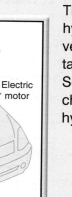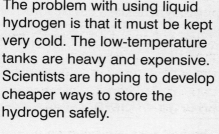

LH$_2$ tank
Fuel cells
Electric motor

9.22 *Diagram of Necar 4*

The problem with using liquid hydrogen is that it must be kept very cold. The low-temperature tanks are heavy and expensive. Scientists are hoping to develop cheaper ways to store the hydrogen safely.

20 What are the advantages of using fuel cells?

21 Describe one disadvantage of fuel cells. Why is this a problem?

Scientists are making great progress developing fuel cell vehicles. Ford's P2000HFC zero-emission vehicle is slightly larger than a Mondeo and weighs 1520 kg. It can accelerate from 0 to 62 mph in 14 seconds (compared with 10.7 seconds for the 1.8 Mondeo and 14.7 for the diesel engine version).

Fuel cells already power zero-emission buses in Vancouver and Chicago. A 12 m vehicle powered by a fuel cell can cover up to 250 miles. And of course the electricity from a fuel cell could just as easily provide power for your home. You could even predict a scenario in which your house is plugged into your car for its power!

22 Explain how Cyrus Harding's prediction has come true.

Find out more about zero emission cars at ▶ **www.scienceweb.co.uk**

Energy and living things

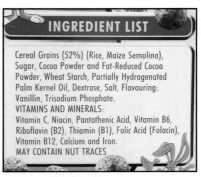

9.23 *Ingredients in a breakfast cereal*

23 What is respiration?

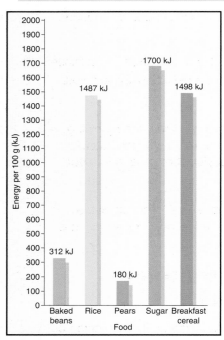

9.24 *The energy content of different foods*

24 What substances in food provide the most energy?

25 Draw an energy chain to show how energy gets from the Sun to a moving car.

Like other animals, humans get their energy from the food they eat. Too much food and you will put on weight. Too little food, or the wrong sort, means you may not grow properly and may get tired all the time.

Food is a fuel just like coal or oil. If you set fire to food it will give out heat. Some foods contain more energy than others. The packaging on food often states exactly how much energy you will get if you eat it. The amount of energy is listed in units called **Joules** (or sometimes in calories). The energy from food is released inside the living cells of our bodies – though not with a flame. The energy is released in a series of chemical reactions called **respiration**. The oxygen we breathe in is used in these reactions. Respiration provides us with energy to grow and for all our activities.

Plant energy

Most plants get their energy direct from the Sun by a process called **photosynthesis**. They absorb the Sun's rays and use carbon dioxide gas from the air to generate the energy they need to grow. They are really storing the Sun's energy in themselves as **carbohydrates**. When we eat plants we take their stored energy into ourselves.

Energy chains

No matter where you start, you will always trace energy back to the Sun. All the energy we use first came from the Sun.

We can show the links on an energy chain diagram.

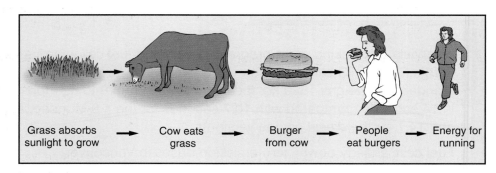

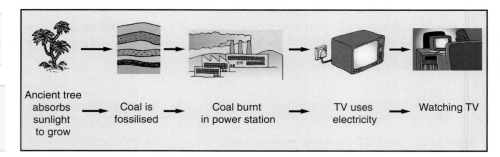

Questions

1 North America is a continent with many means of generating electricity. There are oil and gas fields which supply fuels. There are fast-flowing rivers with large volumes of water. There are strong winds blowing almost continuously from the mountains. There are hot pools of mud and heat energy from the ground.

a Name the method for generating electricity using water.

b Name the method for generating electricity using heat from the earth.

c Why would all these be called renewable energy sources?

d Name one non-renewable fuel from the above paragraph.

2 Electricity is generated in a power station. Many people believe electricity is a clean energy source but some people believe it to be a hidden polluter.

a Explain why some people believe electricity to be a clean energy source.

b Explain why some believe electricity to be a hidden polluter.

c Why would hydroelectric power generation be a clean option for producing electricity?

3 We heat our homes using many different types of fuels.

a What is a fuel?

b What is a fossil fuel?

c Name a fuel used to heat our homes.

4 Describe how oil or coal is formed.

5 Burning fossil fuels causes pollution.

a Name two gases formed that are pollutants.

b When fuels burn carbon combines with another element. What is that element?

c What is formed when carbon combines with that element?

d Fossil fuels also contain hydrogen and this forms another waste product. What is that product?

6 Some New Age dwellers use biomass as a fuel source to reduce the level of pollution and to use up waste materials.

a What is biomass material?

b How is it used to release energy?

c What is formed when it is burnt to produce energy?

d Since the product is burnt would you consider this a clean fuel or a pollutant? Explain your answer.

7 Draw an energy chain showing trees growing, then being used in an electricity-generating station and the electricity being used for heat and light.

8 Explain why it is impossible to obtain all the energy contained in a fuel and why so much is wasted.

9 All energy sources have one source.

a Name that one source.

b Explain why it is considered the beginning of all energy chains.

c Name two energy sources that do not rely on photosynthesis.

10 Are fossil fuels still being created on Earth? Explain your answer.

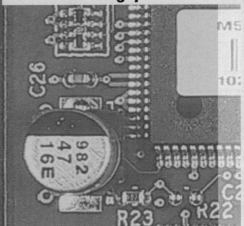

Starting points ▶

Electricity is used to make many everyday items work. You may have carried out work with simple electrical circuits and know that a complete circuit is always needed to makes things work. Some materials allow electricity to flow through them and these are called **conductors**. Other materials do not let electricity flow and these are called **insulators**.

We use circuit diagrams to show how the parts in a circuit are connected. Symbols are used to represent the different components used. These make it easier to draw a circuit.

Many useful experiments about the properties of electricity can be done using a simple circuit.

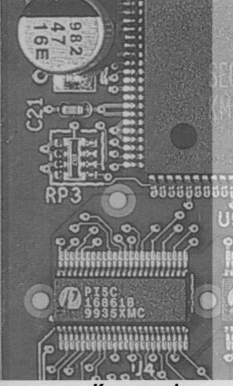

Learning objectives ▶

Reading this unit will help you to learn about and understand the ideas and processes involved in electric circuits:

That a complete circuit is needed for electric components to work.

About how to check a faulty circuit.

How electrical current and electrical energy are measured.

That cells and batteries produce electricity from a chemical reaction.

How we can use models to explain how the electrical current in a circuit behaves.

That electrical devices resist the flow of electric current.

How we can control the current flowing in a circuit using variable resistors.

How a fuse works.

About the difference between series and parallel circuits.

That nerves in animals carry electrical impulses which control how they act.

Key words ▶

ammeter	conductor	impulse	resistor
amps	current	insulator	series circuit
battery	defibrillator	nervous system	variable resistors
bulb	dimmers	neurone	voltmeter
cell	electrons	pacemaker	volts
circuit	fuse	parallel circuit	

Learning summary ▼

This poem summarises the key learning points in this unit.

Electricity without it where would we be?
Back to the 19th century.
No heart pacemaker or sandwich toaster,
No Christmas lights, no TV,
No mobile phones, no gadgetry.

Electricity.
It was discovered!
To make the first battery.
Volta between different metals switching,
Galvani saw frogs' legs twitching.

Electricity!
How can it flow from A to B?
Incredibly small, electrons drift randomly.
Until voltage pushes them from A to B.
Ammeter for the flow or current to 'see'.

What are bulbs?
Resistors that glow, you can see.
Resistors make the flow
Of electrons less easy .... so?

Are there other resistors?
Certainly!
The volume controls on your TV
Are variable ones but that's not all.
Dimmer light switches at concerts and at home
   on the wall.

Different circuitry?
Serial circuit with bulbs one after the other
To squeeze through up to four bulbs.
Think how hard that must be
Producing only dim light by which to see.

Different circuitry?
With parallel bulbs electrons flow one way
   or the other
To squeeze through one bulb.
Wow! How much easier that must be!
Producing bright light by which we can see.

Fuses for what?
Fuses are thin: so they get hot easily.
Too much current and they melt.
No more electrons flow.
Saving us from electrical jolts
From the current, from the volts.

Does electricity flow in you and me?
Certainly!
From eye through nerve to brain
For us to see.
From brain to heart the pulse to steady.
For action we are ready.

Try writing a poem to summarise other units.

A circuit problem

1 Write down some reasons why the torch might not work.

2 What could have been the problem with the torch?

3 Why would that have stopped the bulb lighting up?

4 What is a complete circuit?

5 Explain what happens when the torch switch is turned 'off'.

6 Why is the torch covered with plastic?

It's Jo's birthday and she opens a present. Inside is a torch. Jo quickly puts a **battery** in the torch and pushes the switch. To her surprise the torch does not work. Why?

Taking the battery out, Jo tests it using a piece of wire connecting the base of the torch to the side of a spare **bulb** that has its base touching the top of the battery. This completes a **circuit** and the bulb lights. Jo has shown that the battery is a live one.

Jo takes out the bulb from the torch and replaces the spare bulb with the torch bulb and connects it to the battery. Again the circuit is complete and the bulb is lit. Well, that's strange! Jo puts the bulb back in the torch and puts the battery in. The torch is switched on again. This time the bulb lights. 'Well, that's a mystery,' thinks Jo.

For electricity to be useful, it must be controlled so that it flows where we want it. We do this by using **conductors** and **insulators**. Jo's torch is a good example of this. When the torch is working, electricity comes from the battery, but won't make the bulb light unless it can flow back to the battery. We say it needs a complete **circuit** to flow through.

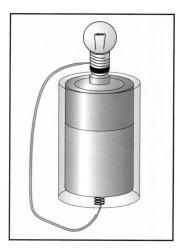

10.1 *A battery-testing circuit*

The electric current flows from the metal button at one end of the battery, and into the bulb, causing the metal filament inside to get hot and light up. The current comes out of the side of the bulb. It flows through the metal body of the torch, and back to the battery through the spring.

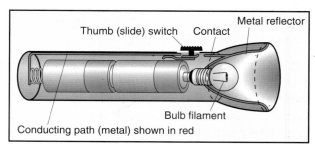

Thumb (slide) switch   Contact   Metal reflector

Bulb filament

Conducting path (metal) shown in red

10.2 *A section through a torch showing a circuit*

Investigating circuits

In school, Jo is investigating how circuits work. She wants to fit electric light bulbs into a doll's house as a project in technology. She makes up a simple circuit with one **cell**, one switch and two bulbs. When she presses the switch down the bulbs light up, so the circuit works. She draws a diagram of the circuit using symbols to represent the different parts.

10.4 *A simple circuit*

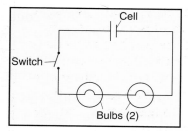

10.5 *A circuit diagram of a cell, switch and two bulbs*

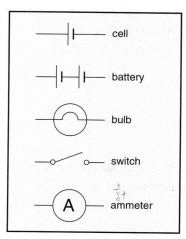

10.3 *Circuit symbols for cell, battery, bulb, switch and ammeter*

The doll's house has four rooms in it, so Jo needs to add two more bulbs to her circuit. She connects the bulbs end to end in a **series circuit**. She is disappointed. The bulbs light up, but only just. They are far too weak. Jo will have to try again. She wonders if there was enough electricity flowing in the circuit to light the bulbs properly.

She goes back to the two bulb circuit, but this time she puts an ammeter in the circuit as well. An ammeter is a device that measures how much **current** flows. The units are measured in **amps** (A). To measure the current the ammeter is connected into the circuit so that current flows through it.

Using the ammeter Jo measures how much current was flowing in the two-bulb circuit. It measures 0.6 A. She checks the reading by moving the ammeter to other places in the circuit, first between the bulbs, then on the left of the circuit. The reading is the same all the way round. The electricity is not being used up as it goes round – just as much flows back into the battery as comes out.

Now Jo tries the four-bulb circuit again. This time the current reading is lower. It is only 0.3 A. There is less current flowing in the circuit. And the bulbs are still very dim.

It's more difficult for the current to flow through four bulbs in series than it is through two, so not as much current flows and the bulbs are dimmer. It is as if the bulbs **resist** the flow of electric current. They seem to make it hard for current to pass through them and so the more there are the harder it is.

7 Draw a circuit diagram of Jo's four-bulb circuit.

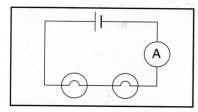

10.6 *A circuit diagram with a cell, two bulbs and an ammeter, all in series*

8 Why do you think adding more bulbs makes them all dimmer?

9 How do you think Jo could make the bulbs brighter?

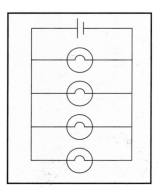

10.7 *A diagram of a parallel circuit with one cell and four bulbs*

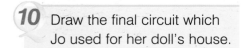
10 Draw the final circuit which Jo used for her doll's house.

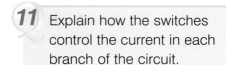
11 Explain how the switches control the current in each branch of the circuit.

In fact all electrical components resist the flow of current. The greater the **resistance** of a component, the harder it is for current to flow through it.

The resistance of a piece of wire is very low – it is easy for current to flow through it. The resistance of a bulb is higher, making it a bit harder for current to flow. The resistance of a piece of plastic is extremely high. It is very difficult for current to flow though it, which helps to make it a good insulator.

Jo needs to find another way of getting the four bulbs to light brightly. It would be good if she could, because that would mean having a bulb in each room – two downstairs and two upstairs.

Her teacher shows Jo how to make a circuit with the bulbs in separate loops. This is called a **parallel circuit**.

She tries setting up the bulbs this way. She is very pleased, because each of the bulbs is bright. Again she uses an ammeter to find out what is happening to the current in the circuit.

The current flowing through each branch of the circuit is less than the current flowing out of the cell. It seems that the current splits up as it goes through a branch, and flows back together where the branches join. Each bulb is bright because the current in each branch meets little resistance to its flow.

Jo is pleased with her new circuit because the bulbs are all bright. She also realises that by putting a switch in each branch of the parallel circuit, she can make each bulb switch on and off without affecting the others.

Switches

Switches help to control where an electric current can flow in a circuit. Inside a switch there is a piece of metal which can be moved into two positions. In one position (open) the metal is moved away from the wires in the circuit, so that the circuit is incomplete. In the other position (closed) the metal touches both the wires in the circuit, which is then complete.

When a switch is turned off (opened) there is a break in the circuit and no current can flow through that part of it. When a switch is turned on (closed) a complete circuit is made and current can flow through the switch and around that part of the circuit.

Find out more about electric circuits at ▶ **www.scienceweb.co.uk**

HISTORY BOX

Early ideas about electricity

Scientific discoveries are often made as a result of an accident. Luigi Galvani was an Italian scientist who lived between 1737 and 1798. He worked at Bologna University where his main area of interest was anatomy; bodies and organs fascinated him. The story goes that, one day, Luigi had a dead frog in the house, either for food or scientific study. As his wife was clearing the kitchen, she dropped the tray with the frog on it and caused a sharp knife to cut through its rear legs. The legs twitched repeatedly, and she screamed with fright. Luigi was fascinated though, and wondered why the legs behaved like this.

First of all he found out what happened when he probed a frog's leg, either in the muscle or a nerve, using a brass needle. He discovered that the leg would contract, or pull back. He also noticed that the energy from lightning would make dead frogs' muscles twitch.

Galvani then made a very important discovery. When he was wiring up the frog's legs for the lightning experiment, using different metals for each link, the legs started to twitch even before the lightning struck. To explain this, he came up with the idea of 'animal electricity' – the idea that the animal itself was a supply of electricity. After all, he argued, the only other things in the circuit are bits of wire – it must be the animal that the electricity is coming from. He wrote about his experiments in 1791, mentioning the two metals and the need for moisture.

His friend Alessandro Volta (1745–1827) worked in the University of Padua. He became fascinated by Galvani's experiments, and tried them out for himself. He too found that the frogs' legs twitched, but he noticed that the experiment only worked if two different metals were connected to the legs. Volta argued that it was the different metals, not the frog, that caused the electrical current. The dead animal was only showing that there was electricity there.

In 1800, Volta demonstrated that it was the metals which made electricity by making the first **battery**. Alternate layers of silver and zinc were separated by thick paper soaked in a strong salt solution. This amazing invention, called a **voltaic pile**, made the study of electricity possible since it made large quantities of electricity.

A disc of silver, paper soaked in brine and a disc of zinc make up a single unit known as a **cell**. Repeated numbers of cells are called a battery. As a result of his work, Volta published a list of metals in order of their electricity-producing strength.

Although Volta had shown that the electricity in Galvani's early experiments was caused by the use of two different metals, Galvani did not give up on his ideas. He later discovered that animal tissue *is* a source of electricity – this is how nerves and muscles work.

10.8 *Galvani's experiments with frogs' legs*

12 Why do you think the frog's legs twitched?

10.9 *The voltaic pile*

13 How did Galvani's experiments give Volta his idea?

14 How was Volta's battery different from those we use to power tools and torches today?

Cells and batteries

10.10 *Different types of electric cell*

15 What is the difference between a cell and a battery?

Many electrical devices we use today work from electricity supplied by a cell such as the ones shown in Figure 10.11. Although we often call them batteries, they are really cells because they are made from a single metal unit. Modern cells work in the same way as the voltaic pile. There is no liquid in a modern cell because this would make it too heavy to carry around. Instead moist chemicals or a paste with different metals or carbon are used. The chemical reaction produces electricity which is conducted along a metal wire.

A car battery is different. It is a true battery. It is made from several cells which are connected. Each individual cell in the car battery is made from two strips of metal and sulphuric acid. The cells are connected by wire. By adding cells together in this way more energy is given to the electricity they produce.

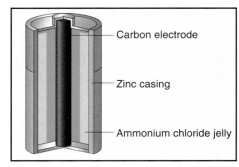

10.11 *Diagram of section through an electric cell*

The energy provided by a battery is measured in **volts** (V), named after Alessandro Volta. One way of thinking about this is to imagine that the cell pushes electric current when it is connected in a circuit. This push is what makes the current flow. The bigger the voltage of a cell, the bigger the push, or the energy, it gives to the current.

We can use a **voltmeter** to measure the energy in an electric current. The measurements are made in volts. Most cells and batteries have the voltage written on the side. This tells you how hard they push a current. When cells are connected together in a series, the push given by each cell is added together, so the current has more energy. The three cells in the picture each give a push of 1.5 V.

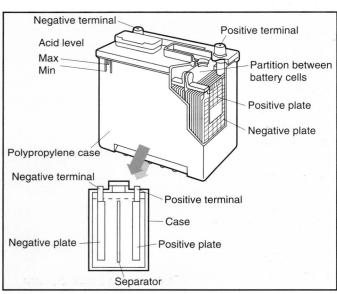

10.12 *Diagram of section through a car battery*

16 What is the total 'push' provided by the three cells?

17 A car battery produces 12 V. How many 1.5 V cells would give the same 'push' to a current?

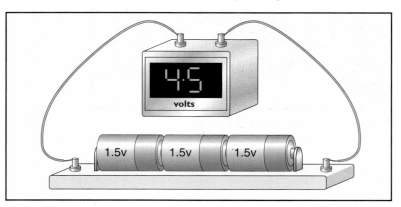

10.13 *When cells are in series their voltage is added*

Before the voltmeter

In the early days of electricity, an English scientist called Henry Cavendish was keen on electricity. He carried out many experiments to find out how electricity worked. But he had no way of measuring the electricity he was investigating – the voltmeter had not yet been invented. Instead he would test an electric current by giving himself an electric shock and seeing how much pain he felt!

Ideas about electric currents

Although they could make electricity with batteries, early scientists were very puzzled when it came to explaining electricity. The best idea they had was that an electric current was an invisible fluid which flowed through wires. To make it easier to talk about electric current, they decided that the fluid flowed from the + end of a cell, and went back in through the – end.

In 1897 Sir Joseph Thomson, a physicist, made a startling discovery that changed our way of thinking about electricity. He discovered that the basic units of matter – atoms – contain tiny particles which carry an electric charge. He called these particles **electrons**. We now know that the current moving through a circuit is made up of electrons. Scientists also believe that the current of electrons comes out of the – end of a cell, and returns through the + end. Electrons can move between the particles that make the metal wire in a circuit. The wire is a conductor because it allows electrons to move through it. The wire is covered with plastic which is an insulator. Electrons cannot move easily between the particles in an insulator. This wire is like a road or path and electricity can move along it if it is complete but if there is a gap the flow is stopped.

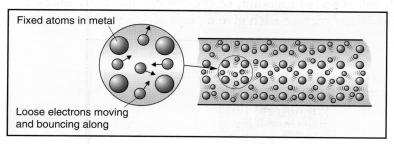

Fixed atoms in metal

Loose electrons moving and bouncing along

10.14 *The movement of electrons in a conductor*

18 What are the particles that make up an electric current?

19 Why do they move through a wire?

20 What do amps measure?

Thinking about electric circuits

You might find it easier to imagine what is going on in an electric circuit by comparing it with a model central heating circuit. The water is pumped through a series of pipes as it flows around the circuit. The pump pushes the water around. Where it flows through thinner pipes in the radiator the current slows down because the pipes resist its flow. Heat from the water is used to make the radiator warm. The water flowing back to the pump is cooler, but there is the same amount as flowed out of it.

21 Which part of the water circuit is like a cell or battery in an electric circuit?

22 Which part is like a bulb?

23 Which part is like the wires?

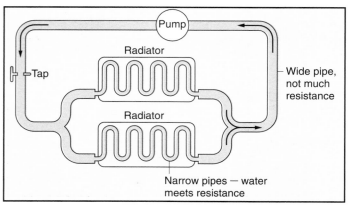

10.15 *A water circuit*

If you have ever watched commuters moving along a corridor and up escalators on their way to work you have found another way of explaining currents. The commuters join others already moving along the corridor in the same direction.

10.16 *Workers moving up a crowded escalator*

24 How is the movement of pupils like electrons flowing through a wire?

At points where the corridor is wide you can see people moving easily. Some pass each other, moving with more energy than others who move slowly. Where the corridor is narrow, such as on an escalator, the people have to squeeze up close together and they take longer to pass. They get hot moving through the narrow space. At the top, the corridor gets wider and they can move easily.

The people's movement is similar to an electric current. The escalator is like the wire conducting electricity. The flow of people is like a current. The push of the people is like the voltage. The narrow part of the journey – the escalator – acts as a resistance to the smooth flow.

Resistance effects

Bulbs

When electricity tries to pass through a bulb the long, thin wire inside produces high resistance to the flow of electricity. This thin wire is called a filament. The high resistance is caused because the wire is very long. There is not much space for electrons to move and it is coiled to fit inside the bulb and the material is not a good conductor. These three things slow the electrons down and energy is transferred as heat and light.

To stop the filament in a bulb from melting, the metal used is tungsten which glows white hot at 2700°C. In air the white hot wire will react with oxygen and act as an insulator. To stop this happening the air inside the bulb is replaced with an unreactive gas like argon. The higher the current the more electrons will be slowed, the more energy will be transferred and the brighter the lamp.

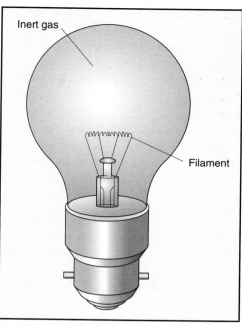

10.17 *An electric bulb*

25 Why are bulbs filled with argon gas?

Fuses

Sometimes, when a current passes through a thin wire, the wire gets so hot that it melts and breaks. This is what a **fuse** is designed to do. Fuses are fitted to many electrical appliances in the home. Every plug has a fuse in it. The fuse has a piece of thin wire running through it. This has a high resistance to electric current. If the right amount of current is flowing the fuse lets it through. But if there is a fault in the circuit and too much current flows the fuse blows. This helps to protect us from dangerous circuits because as the metal fuse melts the circuit is broken and the electric current can no longer flow.

10.18 *Fuses*

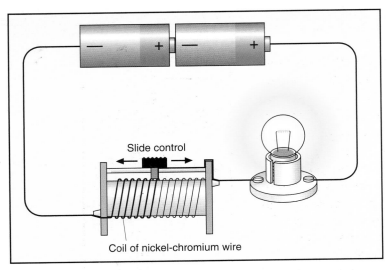

10.19 *A dimmer circuit*

Slide control

Coil of nickel-chromium wire

Dimmers

At a stage show or concert you may have seen that the lights can be controlled to make them brighter or dimmer. The lights are controlled by **dimmers**. These have a sliding plastic handle. The handle surrounds a metal ring on a metal rod. A metal pointer from the ring touches a long metal coil which in turn is connected to an electric current. The coil is a long piece of resistance wire wound around an insulator. The longer the coil the more resistance there is. The pointer moves along the coil changing the length of the resistance wire. These are **variable resistors**, because the resistance can be changed.

As the pointer touches the coil current flows from the coil into the metal bar and to the light. If the pointer is close to the beginning of the coil there is little resistance, so a lot of electricity can flow to the light bulb and it will shine brightly. If the pointer is close to the end of the coil then the resistance of the coil will stop a lot of electricity getting to the bulb and it will glow dimly. Sliding the pointer along the coil changes the resistance and makes the light brighter or dimmer.

Dimmer switches can be found in homes instead of a normal switch. This time the coil is bent into a circle. As you turn the dimmer switch up the light gets brighter because the resistance is reduced. The same arrangement is found in some electrical appliances like a drill or food processor to make the motor run faster or slower.

26 The volume control of a TV is worked by a variable resistor similar to a dimmer. Explain how you think it might work.

10.20 *Inside a domestic dimmer switch*

Living electricity

Electricity isn't only found in circuits and machines. It is important for making your body work properly. Your **nervous system** works by using electricity to communicate between different parts of your body. The main parts of your nervous system are your brain and spinal cord.

Your sense organs pick up information about what is going on in the world around you, and inside your body. They send messages along nerves to your brain, letting it know what is going on. The brain decides how you should react. Your brain controls most of your body movements by sending messages to your muscles. These messages are tiny bursts of electricity that travel along nerve fibres. Each burst of electricity is called an **impulse**. Each nerve fibre or **neurone** is a specialised cell. It has many fine branches connecting to other neurones. Some neurones have a very long thin branch which connects to a muscle. These branches are covered with an insulator to stop the messages leaking out as they pass along the nerve.

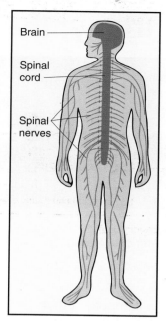

10.21 *The nervous system*

We often have to respond very quickly in dangerous situations. Imagine how quickly a car driver has to act to avoid hitting something that runs onto the road. In a split second a nerve impulse travels from the driver's eyes to his brain, through the neurones there and out along a nerve fibre to his leg muscles making them press on the brakes. Electrical impulses travel very fast along nerves.

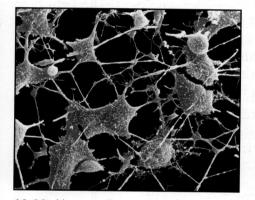

10.22 *Nerve cells*

27 What are your sense organs?

28 Find out how quickly electrical impulses travel along nerves.

Electricity is important for controlling movements and responses in all animals, but some animals have developed a special use for it. They use electricity to keep other animals away, and even to kill them for food. The stingray is a fish that uses electricity to defend itself. It can give any attacking fish a shock of up to 200 V, which will see off most enemies. It also uses its electric shock treatment to stun other fish which are its prey before eating them. The electric eel is one of the most feared South American fish. It can sting its prey up to six times in less than 1/200th of a second. Each sting is an electric shock of up to 500 V – enough to kill a human being!

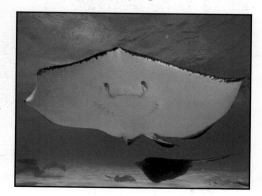

10.23 *A stingray*

Electricity: the heart of the matter

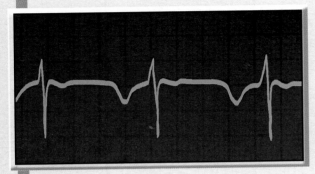

10.24 *An ECG showing the pattern of a heart beat*

29 Why is it important that everyone stands clear when a shock is given?

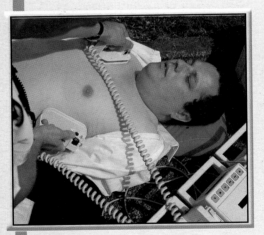

10.25 *Using a defibrillator*

30 Why do pacemakers need a long-life battery?

The body's electrical impulses can be picked up by sensors in special machines and displayed on a monitor. When a person has a heart attack, the heart muscle may not be working properly. A doctor can investigate the electrical impulses in the heart muscles using an ECG (electrocardiogram). She puts sensors on the surface of the chest and these pick up the electrical impulses in the heart. The doctor can tell whether the heart is working properly by studying these pictures.

After a heart attack the patient's heart may stop beating altogether. When this happens doctors can sometimes restart the heart using an electrical machine called a **defibrillator**. You may have seen these being used in a medical drama on TV. The doctor charges up the machine and places two pads on the patient's chest over the heart. Shouting "Clear!" the doctor switches it on. For a split second a current of 20 A and 3000 V passes through the heart. This shock can make the heart muscle contract and start beating again.

Sometimes the heart muscles do not beat at the right rhythm. Doctors can help the heart muscle to work properly using a **pacemaker**. This is an electrical device that sends an electrical impulse to the heart muscle, controlling its rhythm. It helps to maintain a steady heartbeat. The pacemaker is inserted in the patient's body under an armpit and a piece of fine wire is fed along a vein to connect it to the heart. A pacemaker battery goes on working for many years.

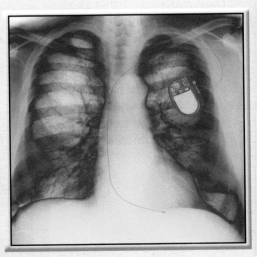

10.26 *Spot the pacemaker*

Questions

1 Mark these sentences true or false.

   a Complete circuits have an open switch.

   b For a circuit to work the wires should be made of a conductor.

   c Complete circuits have a power source to supply the electricity.

   d Complete electrical circuits have a current of electrons flowing.

   e Complete circuits have a current of atoms flowing.

2 Two different circuits are shown below. Sophia notices that when closed each circuit is different.

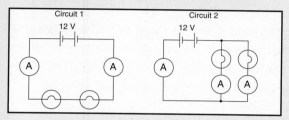

   a What does Sophia observe about the brightness of the bulbs in circuit 1?

   b What does Sophia observe about the brightness of the bulbs in circuit 2?

   c What does Sophia notice about the current in circuit 1?

   d What does Sophia notice about the current in circuit 2?

   e Explain the differences.

3 Below is a circuit for lights in a doll's house.

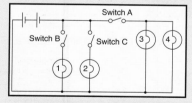

   a One of the bulbs is for the entrance hall. Identify which bulb it is and which switch you would need to close to light it.

   b Which one is for the downstairs room? Identify which bulb it is and which switch you would need to close to light it.

   c Which bulb is for the stairs and which lights a bulb both downstairs and upstairs? Identify which bulb is which and which switch you would need to close to light it.

4 David set up a series circuit with three cells, one switch and a bulb. He added another bulb in series. He noticed the two bulbs were dim. David added another bulb and noted the three bulbs were very dim.

   a Explain why the bulbs got dimmer when more bulbs were added in series.

   b Explain why the bulbs lit up and where the energy was transferred from.

   c Explain what resistance is.

   d What happened to the resistance as more bulbs were added?

   e What would happen if the bulbs were connected in parallel?

5 Batteries have a number such as 3 V printed on the side.

   a What does the V stand for?

   b What instrument would you use to measure that?

   c Is V a measure of current or energy?

6 Explain how a dimmer works to reduce the brightness of a bulb.

7 Electrical circuits are protected by a fuse.

   a Explain how a fuse protects a circuit.

   b What size fuse would be appropriate for a kettle or electric steam iron?

     A 3 A **B** 13 A **C** 5 A **D** 1O A

   c What would happen if you put a 13 A fuse in an appliance which needed a 3A fuse? Explain your answer.

8 It is possible to measure the amount of current in an electrical circuit.

   a Describe how you would connect an ammeter into a circuit.

   b What does an ammeter measure?

   c What would you notice about ammeters connected in each arm of a parallel circuit?

   d What would you notice if you connected two ammeters, one just after the battery and one just after the bulb?

   e Explain the differences.

9 It is possible to measure the strength of an electrical current.

   a Describe how you would connect a voltmeter into a circuit.

   b What does it measure?

   c What would you notice about voltmeters connected in each arm of a parallel circuit?

   d What would you notice if you connected two voltmeters, one just after the battery and one just after the bulb?

   e Explain your answers.

UNIT 11 Forces

Pushing and pulling are examples of forces. They can act on objects to change their speed, direction or shape. We can measure the strength of a force using a force meter. A force is measured in newtons. A force acts in a particular direction. In diagrams, the direction that a force is acting in is shown by an arrow. The longer the arrow, the larger the force.

Gravity is the name of the force which pulls objects down towards the earth. Friction is the force which occurs between two surfaces and can cause moving objects to slow down.

Learning objectives ▶

Reading this unit will help you to know about and understand the following ideas and processes to do with forces and their effects:

About the forces which act on floating objects.

That upthrust is a force which is exerted on an immersed object.

That the density of a substance is its mass divided by its volume.

About the distinction between the mass and the weight of an object.

What causes some objects to float and others to sink in water.

That stretching a material to a limit leads to balancing forces.

That friction is a force which opposes motion.

About some situations where friction is useful and some where it causes problems.

How to measure speed (and its units).

About some factors which affect the stopping of cars.

Key words ▶

air resistance	gravity	unbalanced forces
balanced forces	lift	upthrust
density	lubricant	volume
drag	mass	weight
friction	speed	

This mind map summarises the key learning points in this unit

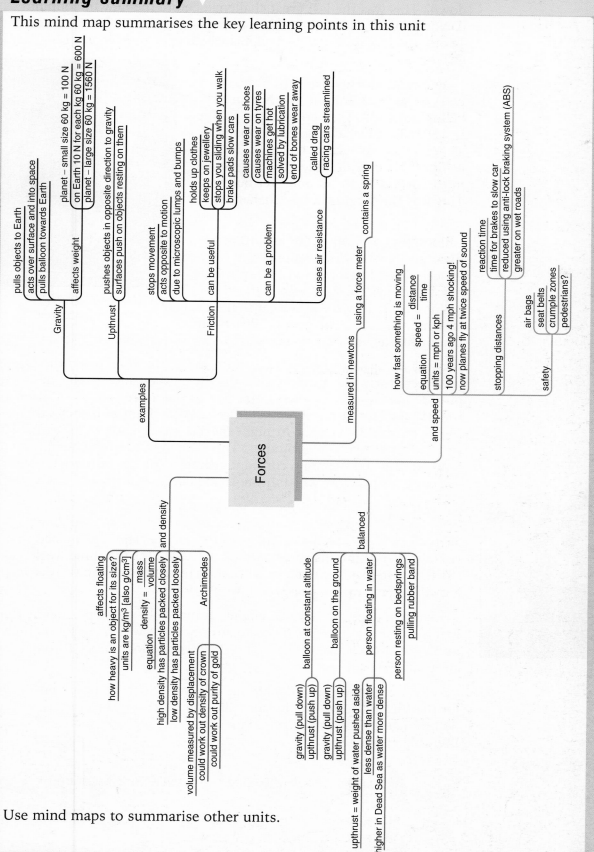

Use mind maps to summarise other units.

The last challenge

Could a balloon travel entirely around the globe without touching down? This was the last great challenge before the new millennium dawned. During 1999 five teams attempted to be the first to succeed. Two of these were the Virgin Global Challenger and the Breitling Orbiter 3.

Per Lindstrand and Richard Branson had crossed the Atlantic in a hot air balloon in 1987. They crossed the Pacific in 1991. To travel around the globe non-stop was the last great challenge. To achieve this they designed the largest and most advanced gas balloon ever built. This was the Virgin Global Challenger.

11.1 *The Virgin Global Challenger balloon*

The cone-shaped envelope of the balloon was over 50 m tall and 40 m in diameter. At the top it contained a spherical cell filled with 31,000 m^3 of a gas called helium. This helped the balloon to float in the air, because helium is lighter than air. The balloon floated in the air like a cork floats on water. The air lifted it up.

It was important to keep the helium gas warm. If it cooled the gas would contract and would reduce the lift on the balloon. The air outside the balloon was very cold. The temperature was –50°C. During the day the Sun kept the temperature of the helium well above this and the balloon floated easily. At night the gas burners were ignited for 10 to 15 seconds every few minutes. This helped to keep the helium up to temperature and maintain constant altitude. The gas burners heated the cone of air below which heated the helium at the top.

The living capsule was about the size of a small caravan. It was completely sealed and pressurised because the air is so thin at an altitude of 12,600 m that humans can't breathe. The capsule had to contain everything the three aeronauts needed for the three weeks of the flight. It also had to store all the waste they produced. It was very crowded – and rather smelly.

A balloon does not have an engine. It moves by being pushed by the winds of the jet stream. These are strong winds which are found high up in the Earth's atmosphere. They help the balloon move through the air at high speed.

Sadly, like many great adventures, this one ended in disappointment for the Virgin Global Challenger team. The Breitling Team succeeded in becoming the first team to circumnavigate the globe in their balloon, Breitling Orbiter 3.

1 Why is helium used in an air balloon?

2 Why was it important to keep the helium warm?

11.2 *The living capsule in the Virgin Global Challenger*

3 How can the wind push a balloon?

Find out more on the Internet at ▶ **www.scienceweb.co.uk**

Getting off the ground

A team of scientists and engineers designed the Virgin Global Challenger. They used their knowledge of forces to help them. They had to think about the forces that would make the balloon float in the air and those that would move it forwards.

Gravity is a force which attracts objects to the Earth. It acts everywhere on the Earth and keeps things on the surface. It acts on objects at a distance, too, so objects in the air or even out in space are attracted to the Earth by this force. The effect of gravity would be to pull the balloon down towards the Earth, but gravity was not the only force affecting the balloon.

Upthrust is a force which pushes objects away from the Earth. It works in the opposite direction to gravity. Surfaces push upwards on objects resting on them. While the balloon was on the ground, the force of gravity was balanced by the upthrust of the surface. The balloon and its capsule stayed put.

Gas particles in the air also create an upthrust. This is sometimes called **lift** and is caused by the gas particles in the air pushing against an object. To make the balloon rise the upthrust needs to be more than the force of gravity. The forces have to be **unbalanced**. If the upthrust is not enough, the downward force of gravity will take over and the balloon will sink to the ground.

When a balloon is floating at a constant altitude, the upthrust of the air and the downward pull of gravity are the same. The forces are **balanced**.

Not all objects float. Many will fall through the air and sink in water. The upthrust of air or water cannot overcome the pull of gravity. Whether an object will float or sink depends on how heavy it is for its size. This is called the **density** of an object.

11.3 *The pull of gravity on a balloon*

11.4 *Balanced forces acting on a balloon on the ground*

11.5 *Forces acting on a rising balloon*

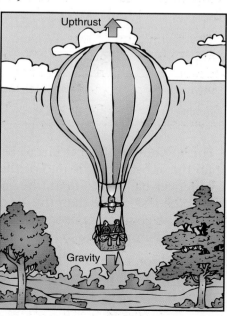

11.6 *Forces acting on a floating balloon*

4 Draw a diagram showing the forces acting on a falling balloon.

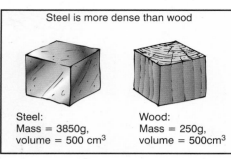

Steel is more dense than wood

Steel:
Mass = 3850g,
volume = 500 cm³

Wood:
Mass = 250g,
volume = 500cm³

11.7 *Steel and wood blocks of the same size*

5 Work out the density of the steel using the formula in the text.

6 A lead weight with a volume of 6 cm³ has a mass of 66 g. What is the density of the lead?

7 Why do gases have such low densities compared to solids? Use the particle theory to explain.

8 If petrol and water are mixed, the petrol floats on top of the water. Can you explain why this is?

9 Why does helium become less dense when it is heated? Clue: think about what happens to its particles.

Explaining density

A block of wood and a block of steel of exactly the same volume weigh different amounts. The steel block weighs more because steel is more **dense** than wood. This is because the particles that make up steel are packed more closely together than the particles in wood. There are more particles to the same volume.

To work out the **density** of a material we must measure the mass of a known **volume** of the substance. If the mass is measured in kilograms (kg) and the volume is measured in cubic metres (m^3), the density is given in kg/m^3. This tells us how many kilograms are in each cubic metre.

Sometimes the mass of a substance is measured in grams (g) and the volume is measured in cubic centimetres (cm^3). Then the density is given in g/cm^3. This tells us how many grams there are in each cubic centimetre.

We can calculate the density of an object using the formula:

$$\text{density} = \frac{\text{mass of object}}{\text{volume of object}}$$

So, for a block of wood with a volume of 500 cm^3 with a mass of 250 g, the density is:

$$\text{density} = \frac{250}{500}$$

$$= 0.5 \text{ g/cm}^3$$

Here are the densities for some materials.

Substance	Density (kg/m³)	Density (g/cm³)
Gold	19,000	19
Lead	11,000	11
Water	1,000	1
Petrol	800	0.8
Air	1.3	0.0013
Helium	0.18	0.00018

For anything to float it has to be less dense than the substance it is in. For the Virgin Challenger balloon to float, the gas inside it had to be less dense than the air outside. This is why the engineers chose helium to fill the balloon. Helium is much less dense than air.

The balloonists heated the gas in the balloon to make it even less dense. This helped it to rise up through the air around it.

11.8 *Firing the burners on the Virgin Global Challenge*

HISTORY BOX

Archimedes the problem solver

Archimedes lived from about 287–212 BC. He was a Greek scientist who enjoyed solving all kinds of problems. He became so famous that kings would consult him over important issues.

The king of Syracuse once set Archimedes a difficult problem. The king had asked his goldsmith to make a solid gold crown. However, when the crown was delivered the king suspected that the goldsmith had added other cheaper metals, such as silver, to the gold. He thought the goldsmith had kept some of the precious metal for himself. The king asked Archimedes to work out exactly how much gold was in the crown.

The crown weighed exactly the same as the gold the King had given the goldsmith. But gold is more dense than silver. A kilogram of gold takes up less space than a kilogram of silver. So Archimedes realised that if silver or any other metal had been added to the gold, the crown would have a greater volume than a crown made of pure gold.

Archimedes had to find the volume of the crown. At that time nobody had worked out how to measure volume.

11.9 *An ancient gold crown*

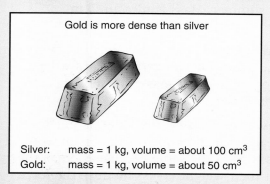

Gold is more dense than silver

Silver: mass = 1 kg, volume = about 100 cm³
Gold: mass = 1 kg, volume = about 50 cm³

Archimedes had noticed that when he got into a bath, the level of the bath water rose. He had seen this many times but had never thought about why it happened before. Now he realised. His body was displacing (taking the place of) the water and pushing it out of the way. He realised that if he put the crown in water, the volume of water it displaced would be the same as the volume of the crown. The story goes that he leapt naked out of his bath and ran down the street shouting "Eureka!" (which means "I have found it!").

By weighing the crown he could calculate the density of the metal. If the goldsmith had added other metals to the gold, the density of the crown would be less than the true density of gold. History does not record whether the king of Syracuse's goldsmith was honest or not.

10 Why do you think it was difficult to find the volume of the crown?

11 How could Archimedes work out the volume of the crown?

12 If silver had been used to replace some of the gold, what would Archimedes have found when he weighed the crown?

Mass and weight

11.10 *Neil Armstrong and Buzz Aldrin on the Moon*

On Earth we exert 10 N of weight per 1 kg of mass

Mass = 60 kg
Weight = 600 N

"That's one small step for a man, one giant leap for mankind!" With these words Neil Armstrong became the first man to walk on the Moon in July 1969 – and his footprints are still there to this day!

For anyone who saw the television pictures of Neil Armstrong and Buzz Aldrin, or any of the astronauts who followed them, the most surprising thing was to watch them bounding around on the Moon's surface. They could jump 2–3 metres in a single stride! Some people even believed that the astronauts' giant leaps proved that there was no gravity on the Moon. Of course they were wrong. If there was no gravity on the moon, the lunar module and the astronauts would not have been able to stay on the surface at all. All planets and moons have gravity – but some have more than others.

The amazing bouncing astronauts could leap several metres with every stride because the gravity on the Moon is so weak. It was as if they weighed only one-sixth of their normal weight.

It's easy to get confused by the idea of an adult astronaut weighing only as much as a toddler. To make the whole thing clearer we have to distinguish between **mass** and **weight**.

Mass is the total amount of stuff in your body. It doesn't change unless you grow or get fatter or slimmer. Mass is measured in kilograms.

Weight is the force you exert downwards and is an effect of gravity. It is measured in newtons. The Earth's gravity exerts 10 N of weight (downwards force) for every kilogram of your mass, so a 60 kg person, for example, will weigh 600 N on Earth.

On the Moon gravity is much weaker because the Moon is much smaller than the Earth. This means that the same 60 kg person would only weigh 100 N. The body mass stays the same because there is the same amount of matter in it but their weight is less because the force of gravity is smaller on the Moon. The pull of gravity differs on other planets. On Jupiter, for example, the pull of gravity is 26 N for every kilogram of mass.

13 What would a 60 kg child weigh on Jupiter?

14 Why do you think gravity is stronger on Jupiter?

Weight loss in water

You don't have to go to the Moon to experience weight loss. The same effect occurs when you go swimming.

We can use Archimedes' idea to explain why things weigh less in water than they do in the air.

Archimedes' principle says that when an object is put into water it pushes aside a volume of water equal to its own volume. The water pushed aside pushes back against the object. This causes an upthrust, pushing the object upwards. The upthrust is equal to the weight of the water pushed aside.

How much weight an object loses when it is in water depends on how much water it pushes aside.

Upthrust is the upward force which keeps you afloat in water. It also makes it easier for you to lift your friend in a swimming pool. The water pushes up on your friend so he weighs less and you do not have to use as much force to lift him as you do out of the water.

Floating in water

Objects will float in water if they are less dense than water. The size of the object does not matter. The trees in the photograph are huge, but they can float because wood is less dense than water. As the tree goes into the water it sinks until the water it pushes aside just equals the weight of the tree. Water takes up less space than wood for the same mass. So there will be some wood left sticking out of the water and it will float. The upthrust from the displaced water equals the weight of the tree.

15 Explain why a block of steel sinks in water.

16 Ships made of steel float. Why do you think this is?

11.11 *Felled trees from a logging camp floating on water*

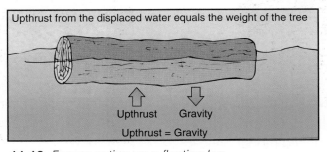

Upthrust from the displaced water equals the weight of the tree

Upthrust   Gravity

Upthrust = Gravity

11.12 *Forces acting on a floating log*

In a liquid more dense than water the upthrust is greater so an immersed object weighs even less than in fresh water. If the upthrust is enough to make the object float completely, then the upthrust is enough to cancel out the weight of the object. If you weighed the object at this point the reading would be zero. This is an example of **balanced forces**.

In the Dead Sea the large amount of dissolved salt makes the water more dense than typical sea water and much more dense than fresh water. This means it supports weight better because it exerts a greater upthrust than fresh water does.

11.13 *Floating in the Dead Sea*

Stretching and weighing

Its not just when you are floating that you feel an upward force working against gravity. When you lie on a bed your weight presses down on the bed. The bed springs are compressed until they are able to support your weight and do not compress any further. They push back against the weight of your body. The forces of you on the bed and of the bed springs on you are balanced.

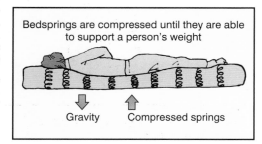

Bedsprings are compressed until they are able to support a person's weight

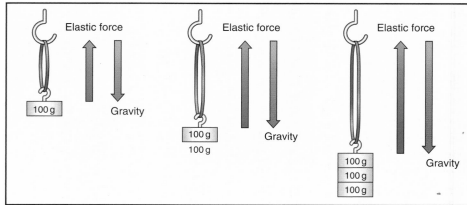

You can also feel an opposing force when you stretch a rubber band and it pulls back with an equal force. The further you stretch it, the more it resists until its force balances your pull and it does not stretch any further. This chart shows how a rubber band stretched as 100 g masses were added to it one at a time.

Mass (g)	Length of rubber band (mm)	Extension (mm)
0	20	0
100	21.5	1.5
200	23	3
300	24.5	?
400	26	?
500	?	?

17 What pattern can you see in the data from the stretched rubber band? Copy the table and fill in the missing data.

18 What do you think happens to the particles inside a rubber band when it is stretched?

A force meter is used to measure the weight of an object. The force meter has a spring inside which stretches when objects are hung from it. The spring stretches more as the mass of the object increases.

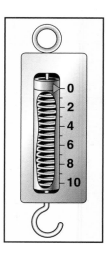

11.14 *A force meter*

Friction

Put any two surfaces together, slide one of them and **friction** will try to stop it moving. Friction is a force that always opposes motion. Even if a surface appears to be perfectly smooth, under a microscope it looks lumpy and pitted. These irregularities dig into each other as the two objects slide and are the reason we get friction.

Friction is a very important force. It helps the surfaces of different objects to cling to each other and prevents them from slipping. Friction helps to hold your clothes up and stops jewellery falling off. It stops you sliding when you walk or run. It lets you pick things up in your hand and is useful when scratching your head. It is friction between the wheel rim and a brake pad that helps to slow down a moving car or bicycle.

Friction forces have a downside too. They make clothes and shoes wear out and tyres bald, blunt the edges of knives and overheat machinery. The outer skin of an aircraft in flight gets very hot even though the surrounding air is −50°C.

Where friction is a nuisance, the best way to stop it is to keep the surfaces apart. **Lubricants** such as oil help to reduce the friction between moving surfaces, such as those in machinery. The oil fills in the tiny pits and smoothes over the lumps on the surfaces so that they will slide over each other as easily as possible. Adding oil to a car's engine cuts down friction between the moving parts and helps the engine work more efficiently.

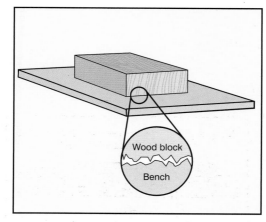

11.15 *Friction between two surfaces (magnified)*

19 Why does friction cause car tyres to wear out?

20 What is the cause of friction in a flying aeroplane?

11.16 *Concorde in flight*

Friction does not only occur between solid surfaces. There is also friction between moving objects and the air around them. This type of friction is called **air resistance**. Air resistance, or **drag**, gets worse as things travel faster. Concorde gets so hot because of air resistance as it flies that it expands. It is about 30 cm longer at the end of a flight than when it took off, even though the air temperature at flying altitude is about −50°C.

Racing cars are designed to travel at high speeds. They have a streamlined shape so that they move through the air easily and suffer less air resistance. Because they travel so fast it is important that they grip the surface of the road as well as possible. The tyres of a racing car are much wider than those on a family car, and they are smooth.

11.17 *Formula One car in the pits*

21 How does having smooth tyres help reduce friction?

22 How would having low density bones help a swimmer?

CLUES IN THE BONES

The forces that act on our bodies affect how our bones grow. Friction on the ends of the bones at the joints can make the bones knobbly and misshapen.

Bones can be of different density and this can tell us about how active a person is. Gymnasts today develop bones with a high density. The frequent impact of jumping and landing builds stronger, denser bones. Swimmers develop lower density bones because they are not supporting their own weight while they exercise.

The force made by the muscles acting on the bones also makes a difference. In the past, archers would spend hours practising with their bows. The repeated action of pulling the bow back with the right arm put extra force on the right shoulder. An archaeologist who digs up the skeleton of an archer will see that the right shoulder joint is bigger because it had to withstand the extra force put on it by the muscles.

Travelling at speed

23 A train travels at 100 km/h. Explain what this means.

11.18 *Motor vehicle from the early 1900s*

The **speed** of an object tells us how fast it is moving. It is given in units that tell us how far an object will travel in a given time, such as miles per hour (mph) or kilometres per hour (km/h). If a car is travelling at a speed of 40 miles per hour, then it will travel 40 miles in 1 hour.

When rail travel became possible many people worried that the human body could not withstand the forces put on it by travelling at speeds as high as 20 mph. Now pilots in jet fighters speed across the sky at Mach 2 or twice the speed of sound.

We can work out the average speed of a vehicle if we know how long it takes to travel a known distance.

$$\text{speed} = \frac{\text{distance travelled}}{\text{time taken}}$$

When the first cars were built around 100 years ago a law was made in the UK that a person carrying a red flag had to walk in front of the car to limit its speed to 4 mph and to warn pedestrians that it was coming. Now many motorists travel at 70 mph for long periods on motorways or limit their speed to 20 mph because of speed bumps or speed cameras in built-up areas. We now expect to be able to drive across the country in a few hours. Going 150 miles from Birmingham to Portsmouth, Cardiff to London, Middlesborough to Liverpool or York to Cambridge might take 3 hours. This would mean that, on average, you travelled 50 miles each hour or at an average speed of 50 mph.

$$\text{Average speed of car} = \frac{150}{3}$$

$$= 50 \text{ mph}$$

We can fly across the Atlantic in less than a day. Flying from London to Florida at an average speed of 600 mph takes 7.5 hours.

Stopping safely

As cars get faster, they also become more dangerous for pedestrians and passengers. Even with seat belts and airbags, passengers travelling in fast cars are likely to be injured in a crash. The Highway Code lists stopping distances for cars travelling at different speeds. The faster the car is travelling, the greater the distance it will cover before it stops.

There are two reasons for this. Firstly, the driver takes a certain time to react to the danger ahead (the reaction time) and the car keeps going while the driver is reacting. Secondly, the brakes have to slow the car down using friction between the brake pads and the wheels. The faster the wheels are turning the longer it will take to stop them. Drivers must think about the need to allow for stopping distances between cars, especially on fast roads such as motorways.

Car speed (km/h)	Thinking distance (m)	Braking distance (m)	Total stopping distance (m)
30	5	5	10
40	7	10	17
50	9	15	24
60	11	22	33
70	13	30	43
80	15	38	53
90	17	48	65
100	19	60	79
110	21	73	94

Many motorways have chevron marking painted onto the road surface at regular intervals. They are painted on sections of road where drivers may be travelling at very high speeds.

At the side of the roads there are signs which warn drivers to keep two chevrons between themselves and the car in front. By following this instruction drivers can be sure that they are far enough away from the car in front to allow safe braking at high speed.

24 Work out how far the plane has flown.

25 What is 'thinking distance'?

26 Why does thinking distance increase as speed increases?

27 Draw a graph of stopping distance (vertical axis) against speed (horizontal axis). What would be the stopping distance at 120 km/h?

28 The stopping distances in the table are for dry roads only. On wet roads the distances can be much greater. Why do you think this is?

11.19 *Chevron markings on road reminding drivers to keep their distance*

Find out more about safe driving at ▶ **www.scienceweb.co.uk**

Safer braking

Scientists and engineers working for motor companies are continually investigating ways of making driving safer. In recent years they have developed many inventions which make driving safer, such as air bags, stronger seat belt materials and crumple zones on cars. They study crashes very carefully using dummies in place of real people to see what happens during a crash. One of the most recent inventions has helped to make braking safer.

If a driver brakes hard, the brakes may hold the wheel so firmly that the wheel stops turning altogether. Unfortunately this doesn't mean the car stops more quickly. If the car is travelling quite fast when the wheels stop turning, the tyres will skid on the road. There is not enough friction between the tyres and the road to stop them skidding. The car may even spin round in the road and end up facing oncoming traffic.

Modern cars are designed with **anti-lock braking systems** (ABS) to help them to stop safely. When the driver hits the brakes, the brake pads push against the wheel to apply friction to stop it turning. If the wheel stops turning completely and the car starts to skid, then the ABS will sense this. It will reduce the force of the brake pads on the wheels. This will stop the car skidding. Then the ABS will immediately apply the full force again until it senses skidding.

So the ABS really turns the brakes on and off repeatedly and very quickly. This way the driver gets maximum force between the brake pads and the wheel to stop the car but avoids skidding. The car will stop in the minimum distance possible and the driver will remain in full control of the vehicle. This is the safest way to stop in the shortest distance.

11.20 *Crash test dummies*

29 What happens when brakes lock?

11.21 *The car has just skidded, leaving marks on the road*

30 How does ABS help to prevent skidding?

Questions

1 A bicycle is a machine which uses many forces.

   a If you stood on the pedals and the bike remained still and upright would the forces be unbalanced or balanced?

   b What is the downward force opposing the upthrust when you sit on a bike seat?

   c Pedalling along a flat smooth road starts by being difficult but then gets easier. Explain why more force is needed to move the bicycle at first.

   d What force slows the bike down when you stop pedalling?

2 Complete the following sentences.
A bag of sugar weighs 1 kg and this is called its............... This is equal to 10...............and this is the...............of the bag of sugar which is the pull of...............

3 Different substances have different densities.

   a Explain what density is.

   b Why is 1 kg of lead denser than 1 kg of feathers?

   c In a fire crawling on the floor is better than walking upright. Explain why this might be.

   d In a mine where there is a large amount of carbon dioxide which can suffocate you, it is recommended that you walk upright. Explain why this advice is given.

4 Two cubes of different metals measure 4 m × 4 m × 4 m. Cube A has a mass of 4 kg and cube B has a mass of 16 kg.

   a Calculate the density of each cube.

   b Which material would be the best to use for an aircraft?

   c Which would be the best to use for divers' weights?

5 Explain why the weight of an object is less on the Moon than it is on the Earth.

6 Kaya and Asha are investigating elastic bands and how they stretch. The results are given in the table.

Force	Extension 1	Extension 2
0	0	0
2	2.2	1.3
4	4.1	2.1
6	6.4	2.9
8	8.1	3.8
10	10.2	4.6
12	12.3	5.5
14	14.1	6.3
16	16.3	7.1
18	18.4	7.9
20	20.9	8.7

   a Draw a graph of the results.

   b Explain what the curves tell us about the elasticity of the two bands.

   c Which band is the most elastic?

   d Assuming the two bands are made from the same sheet of elastic, which band is the thicker? Explain your answer.

7 Della decides to investigate the story of Archimedes and the crown. She puts a lump of metal on the end of a spring balance and notices it weighs 120 newtons (N). When it is put in water the weight changes to 80 N. Explain these results.

8 A skyboarder jumps from an aircraft and is able to surf in the air. After a while she opens her parachute and floats down to Earth.

   a Why doesn't the skyboarder fall quickly?

   b Why does the speed of descent change as the skyboarder moves through the air?

   c Why is the parachute descent so much slower than the fall on the skyboard?

9 A bobsleigh on an ice track covers a distance of 500 m in 20 seconds. Later in the day after 5 runs and when the temperature has dropped to –5°C, the same bobsleigh covers the distance in 15 seconds.

   a What is the speed of the first run?

   b What is the speed of the final run?

   c Which is the fastest run?

   d Explain what might have made that run faster.

   e Which force has been reduced by the weather conditions?

UNIT 12 The solar system

The Sun, the Moon and our planet, the Earth, are very large spherical objects in space. Their positions change with time. This change in position causes shadows to form. Day and night are caused by the spin of the Earth. This spinning makes the Sun appear to move across the sky. The Earth moves around the Sun in an orbit. It takes the Earth a year to complete one orbit. The Moon moves around the Earth in its own orbit. At night time, we can see the Moon because it reflects light from the Sun.

Learning objectives ▶

Reading this unit will help you to know about and understand the following ideas and processes concerning the solar system and the planets:

That the movement of the Earth around the Sun is used to measure time.

About how to explain eclipses.

That the tilt of the Earth causes the different seasons.

That it is possible to see stars because they emit light but planets are only seen when they reflect light.

That the Sun is a star and makes light.

About the positions of the planets of the Solar System and how they compare with Earth.

About how ideas about the Solar System have developed over time and how these ideas have changed our points of view.

Key words ▶

asteroid	inclination	photon	spectrum
atmosphere	Jupiter	planet	star
axis	luminous	Pluto	telescope
comet	Mars	probe	time zone
day	Mercury	satellite	Uranus
eclipse	moon	Saturn	Venus
galaxy	Neptune	season	year
hemisphere	orbit	solar system	

Learning summary ▼

This concept map summarises the key learning points in this unit.

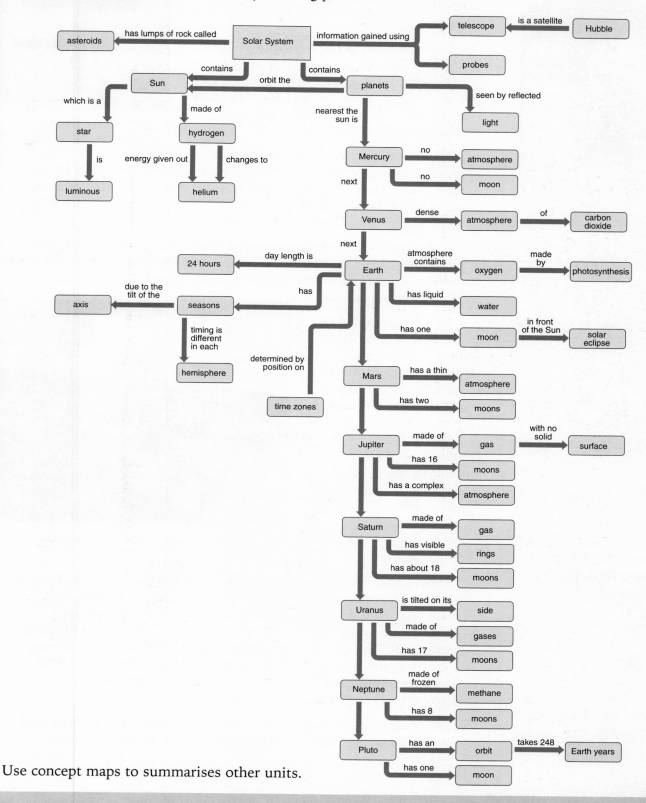

Use concept maps to summarises other units.

Exploring the universe

12.2 *The Mariner space probe*

In December 2000 a new light appeared in the evening sky. Anyone looking to the south east could see the planet Venus rising and a 'star' that seemed to move quickly across the sky.

The new 'star' is the *International Space Station* (ISS). This is a joint venture between many countries, along with the European Space Agency. It is the next stage in space exploration. It is a research station orbiting above the Earth.

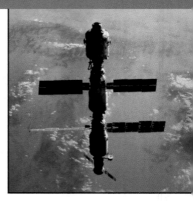

12.1 *The International Space Station*

The last 40 years have been a time of great ventures in space exploration. Scientists from many countries have made many new discoveries about the universe. New **planets**, **stars** and **galaxies** have been observed. We have learnt much more about the already familiar planets of our solar system.

It is not easy to do experiments in space. But by making careful observations and measurements, scientists have made most of the new discoveries. Advances in technology have helped them to make more accurate observations.

1 Why is it difficult to do experiments in space?

Men have walked on the Moon. Spacecraft have landed on the planet Mars. **Probes** have been sent to observe more distant planets in our Solar System. Giant telescopes have been built in space, orbiting the Earth. These have been able to look back in time to the beginnings of the universe itself.

12.3 *Viking space craft landed on Mars in 1976*

2 Which inventions have helped to make observations easier?

3 What is the difference between a star and a planet?

People have always been interested in observing the stars. The History Box opposite tells the story of some of the earliest discoveries made. All of those important early discoveries were made over long periods using only the human eye without the advantages of modern technology. The only known planets were those that could be seen by eye. Then, in the 17th century, scientists began to use the newly invented **telescope** to make their observations. This led to the discovery of more planets in our solar system.

4 What discoveries do you think will be made in the next 50 years?

Nowadays, using giant telescopes in space and computers to analyse observations, who knows what the next great discovery will be?

HISTORY BOX

A timeline of ideas and discovery about space

3000 BC

Egyptians think the Earth is flat. The sky is the arched body of the goddess Nut and the Earth is the body of the god Geb. Between the Earth and sky is a layer of air represented by the god Shu.

500 BC

Aristotle and Pythagoras state that the Earth is at the centre of the universe and is like a ball. This idea lasts until 1500 AD.

380 BC

Democritus observes the Milky Way and states that it is composed of many stars. He also believes the Moon is similar to the Earth.

291 BC

Shih Shen, Gan De and Wu Xien compose star maps which will be used by the Chinese for the next several hundred years.

270 BC

Aristarchus of Samos challenges Aristotle and claims the Sun is the centre of the solar system. He actually estimates the distance from the Earth to the Sun.

240 BC

Chinese astronomers first observe Halley's Comet.

165 BC

Chinese astronomers observe and record sunspots.

200 AD

Ptolemy draws a map of the universe with the Earth in the centre and the Moon and Sun going round the Earth.

1543 AD

Copernicus states that the Earth and other planets orbit the Sun. His theory is not published until after his death.

1600 AD

Johannes Hevelius (1611–1687) sees Mercury as a black dot against the Sun.

1623 AD

Galileo Galilei is imprisoned for openly supporting the Copernican theory of the solar system.

1655 AD

In Holland, Christiaan Huygens (1629–1693) makes telescopes and discovers the rings of Saturn.

1781 AD

In Britain, Sir William Herschel (1783–1822), working with his sister Caroline, hunts for comets. They discover Uranus in the night sky.

1846 AD

Astronomers in England and France believe there is another planet after Uranus. Their calculations precisely pinpoint the new planet. It is discovered by astronomers working in Berlin – the planet Neptune.

1930 AD

In the USA, Clyde Tombaugh (1906–1996) photographs Neptune. In one of his photographs he is surprised to see a faint speck of light that does not stay in the same place. He discovers Pluto.

12.4 *The Milky Way*

12.5 *Halley's Comet from an ancient Chinese drawing*

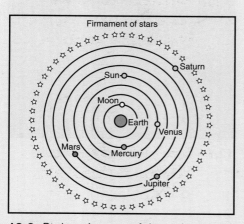

12.6 *Ptolemy's map of the universe*

5 Write a list of planets in the order they were discovered.

6 Why did it take so long for Pluto to be discovered?

Measuring time

From early times, the length of a day was measured by the position of the Sun in the sky. The Sun appears to move across the sky because the Earth spins on its axis. The time taken for one revolution is one **day**. A day is divided into 24 hours. The hour has been used as a unit of time for 5000 years. However, it was not until clocks were invented that minutes were accurately recognised.

During this time people had become dependent upon measuring the seasons using the Sun, stars and planetary movements. This information helped to plan the agriculture calendar. It was important to know the best times to plant and harvest crops.

The Earth takes approximately 365.25 days to make one full revolution around the Sun. This is one **year**. Early astronomers observed how the position of the Sun and stars in the sky changed as time passed during each year. They seem to move across the sky because the Earth is moving around the Sun. Astronomers kept careful records. A year was measured when the Sun rose in a certain place on the horizon.

Although the Sun and stars appear to move across the sky there is one star that does not. The Earth's north always points towards the Pole Star – Polaris. This star does not seem to change its position in the sky.

As the Earth orbits the Sun during the year we experience different **seasons**. The tilt or **inclination** of the Earth on its axis affects the seasons. The Earth is inclined at 23.5° and as it spins the different parts of the Earth's surface receive differing amounts of sunlight. The northern **hemisphere** is warmer than the southern hemisphere during the months of May to August. It is summer in the northern hemisphere and winter in the southern hemisphere at this time. This is because the northern hemisphere is tilted towards the Sun. The Earth's inclination alters the length of days in different seasons.

7 Why do the stars appear to move across the sky?

12.7 *Polaris – the Pole star – in the night sky*

8 Why is January so cold even though the Earth is closer to the Sun?

9 Why do the days have different lengths?

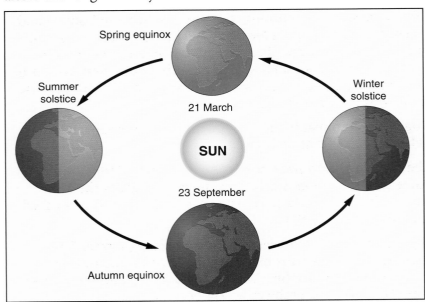

12.8 *Seasonal changes during the Earth's annual orbit around the Sun*

21 March	Spring equinox	Sun at midday is directly above the Equator	Day and night are of equal length all over the Earth
22 June	Summer solstice	Longest day in the Northern hemisphere	At midday the Sun is at its highest point in the sky. It is in its most northerly position
23 September	Autumn equinox	Sun at midday is directly above the Equator	Day and night are of equal length all over the Earth
22 December	Winter solstice	Shortest day in the Northern hemisphere	At midday the Sun is at its lowest point in the sky. It is at its most southerly position in the sky

Earth time – telling the time

Sandi takes a weekend break in New York. She flies from London at 10:30 am and after a 7 hour flight she arrives in New York at 1:30 pm. Her friend Joel remains in London. How can a 7 hour flight mean a 4 hour difference in the time between London and New York?

One turn of any planet on its **axis** is a **day**. On Earth a day is 24 hours. The Sumerians were the first to divide the day into 24 hours 5000 years ago. This movement of the Earth makes it appear that the Sun moves across the sky because things on the Earth's surface move with the Earth.

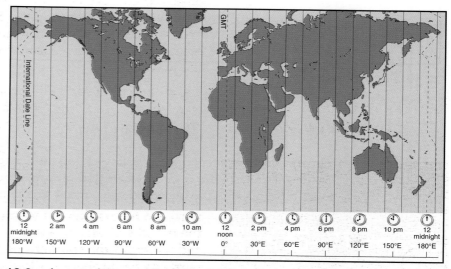

12.9   *A map of the world's time zones*

It is 6:00 am on Saturday morning, the sun is shining in London and for Joel a new day is starting. In New York the time is 2:00 am and it is still dark so Sandi is asleep. Six hours later at noon in London the Sun is overhead and Joel is thinking about lunch, but in New York it is 8:00 am and Sandi is having breakfast. The times are different because of the spinning of the Earth on its axis.

The rising of the Sun marks the start of the day and noon is the point at which the Sun is at its highest.

The globe is divided into **time zones**. An imaginary line that goes through Greenwich, London is called the **meridian** and is the zero point from which times zones start. The time at the meridian is called Greenwich Mean Time (GMT).

Travelling quickly by plane upsets the human sleep pattern. This means when people travel great distances they need some time to settle back into a normal rhythm. This is called jet lag and the greater the distance the bigger the problem jet lag becomes.

10 Why are there time zones on the Earth?

11 What is the time in Hong Kong if the time is 10:00 am in London?

Our solar system

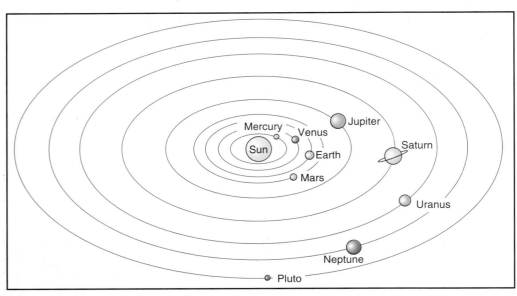

12.10 *Our solar system*

The Earth is a planet orbiting our nearest star, the Sun, along with other planets. The Sun and its planets are called a **solar system**. Although we now take these facts for granted, a few hundred years ago stating these beliefs might have cost you your life.

Dangerous discoveries

In earlier times most people believed that the Earth was the centre of the universe, and that the planets, stars and Sun travelled around it in their own orbits. Only a few hundred years ago this was the accepted view and it was very dangerous to believe anything else.

In Poland, Nicolaus Copernicus, a doctor, lawyer and priest made very careful observations of the night sky. He came to the conclusion that the Earth could not be the centre of the universe. He claimed the Earth was just another planet going around the Sun. He was very careful not to publicise his ideas and they were not published until after his death in 1543.

In Italy some time later, Galileo Galilei was not so lucky. Using a telescope he made close observations of the Sun, Moon and stars. He plotted the moons of Jupiter and the phases of Venus. He made the same claim as Copernicus. This got him into deep trouble with the Roman Catholic Church. A person opposing the teachings of the church could be accused of being a heretic and could be tortured and killed by burning. Galileo's books were banned but he wrote a new book, *Dialogue*. This was a conversation between a wise man (Galileo) and a fool (the Church) about the evidence for the Sun as the centre of the solar system. In 1623 Galileo was put on trial by the Inquisition and under threat of torture he stated that his ideas were wrong. He was then placed under house arrest for the rest of his life.

12 Why were Copernicus' ideas not published until after his death?

13 Why do you think Galileo wrote a book representing both sets of ideas?

14 Do you think Galileo was wise to publish his ideas?

A journey through the solar system

Like all stars, the Sun makes light which then travels away from it through the solar system. The Sun is the source of heat and light for the whole solar system. This is an account of a light particle as it makes this journey.

Hi, I'm **photon**. I'm a particle of light and I move like a wave. At a temperature of 15,000,000°C in the core of the Sun I am created in a reaction in which atoms are changed. The Sun is an atomic generator in which atoms of hydrogen join together in fusion to form atoms of helium. I am one of the by-products along with huge amounts of heat.

The heat at the surface as I pass through has dropped to a cooler 5550°C. On the Sun's surface are cooler areas which are darker in colour and known as sunspots.

Curiously, there is an 11 year cycle during which the number of sunspots increases. The Sun's heat is passed out or radiated across the solar system. On Earth the Sun provides the energy for all forms of life and controls the weather.

In 1862, Father Angelo Secchi analysed light from the Sun and obtained a **spectrum**. Comparing this spectrum of sunlight with other stars he noted they were the same. This indicated that the Sun is a **star**. It is the solar system's own star. It is a **luminous** body because it emits light.

Passing through the Sun's surface close to two sunspots I can feel strange pulls. This is the opposing magnetism of the two sunspots which attract each other. This confused magnetism is due to the furiously swirling gases and their electric charges.

Suddenly the sunspots release a huge bolt of energy and I am thrown into space. The charge of energy continues and a day later will cause interference on radios on Earth. It sets me on my wanderings across the solar system, past the planets and on into space.

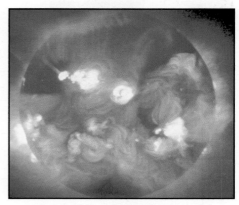

12.11 *An X-ray light image taken by the Japanese Yohkoh satellite*

15 Why is the Sun a star and not a planet?

Mercury

57.9 million km from the Sun, a dark, airless planet with a sky that is permanently black and filled with stars comes into view. This planet spins upright with an inclination of 0°. It is the fastest orbiting planet in the solar system but revolves very slowly on its axis. Battered and baked on one side, this is **Mercury**. No need for a coat on the daylight side since the temperature is about 370°C and can reach 430°C. Lead would melt here and it would be impossible to use a thermometer because the metal would boil.

On the side away from the Sun it is night and the temperature is −170°C, so cold some gases in Earth's **atmosphere** would turn to liquid. A day on Mercury lasts 176 Earth days and a year is 88 Earth days.

12.12 *Mercury*

12.13 *Venus*

16 Why are the days and years on Mercury different from those on Venus?

17 Draw your idea of the surface of Mercury and Venus.

18 What makes a year on Mercury and Venus shorter than on Earth?

19 How much bigger than Mercury is Venus?

20 What are the things that make Earth so good for life to develop?

Mercury is the same density as Earth. This heaviness is due to an interior of very heavy metals, possibly iron. Mercury has a diameter of 4878 km and is only 0.38 the size of Earth. This smallness means its mass is only 0.055 that of Earth.

In 1974 and 1975 a spacecraft called *Mariner 10* from Earth passed close by Mercury and photographed it. Like *Mariner 10* I think I will pass this planet by.

Venus

108.2 million km from the Sun and the next planet, Venus, seems to be different from others. It is revolving in the opposite direction from the others so here the Sun would rise in the west and set in the east. I will need to judge carefully whether I should land on this planet.

Light photons have a favourite way of travelling. We bounce off the surface or atmosphere. You can see Venus from Earth because of the light reflected off the surface. Venus rises in Earth's evening sky and is very bright. Planets can only be seen when they reflect light.

Venus spins very slowly at a very small inclination of 3°. A day here lasts 243 Earth days and a year is 225 Earth days. With a diameter of 12,103 km it is similar in size and density to Earth. Its mass is 0.81 of Earth so its rocks must be different.

Pale yellow clouds of sulphuric acid hide the surface of the planet. These form drops which fall to the surface as acid rain. The atmosphere creates a furnace-like heat because of the carbon dioxide, which traps the Sun's heat like a greenhouse. Temperatures here reach 470°C. Once through the unpleasant atmosphere the surface of Venus is covered with active volcanoes and dry rocks which are so hot that they glow.

This is no place for life. In 1990 *Magellan*, a spacecraft from Earth, succeeded in sending back photos of this corrosive place. A quick bounce off the cloud surface, I think, and I'll pass on to the next planet.

Earth

149.6 million km out from the Sun and this planet is another odd one. Earth spins in the same direction as Mercury but is bright blue with white clouds, which constantly shift around the surface.

It spins on its axis at an angle of 23° and takes 1 Earth day (23 hours 56 minutes) to make one full turn. One revolution around the Sun will take it one year (365 days). It has a diameter of 12,756 km and an average temperature of 15°C.

12.14 *Earth*

Earth is the only planet to support an abundance of life. It has liquid water and an atmosphere of oxygen. I could get used to this and stay here. Some of my fellow photons are busy giving energy to life by powering photosynthesis.

Earth's Moon

The planet Earth has a moon. This moon is thought to be the result of a collision between Earth and another planet. The Moon circles the Earth in an anticlockwise direction once every 27 days. Because it takes the same time to make one turn on its axis it always keeps the same face to the Earth. This face seems to change in size throughout a month.

21 Keep a diary of the phases of the Moon over the next month.

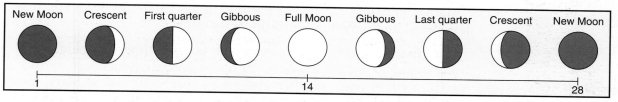

| New Moon | Crescent | First quarter | Gibbous | Full Moon | Gibbous | Last quarter | Crescent | New Moon |

1   14   28

The Moon rises in the east and sets in the west just like the Sun. It is about a quarter of the size of Earth. When Earth and the Moon are in line with the Sun, the Moon can pass between Earth and the Sun and a **solar eclipse** occurs.

12.15 *The phases of the Moon*

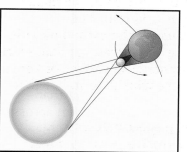

12.16 *Diagram of a solar eclipse*

12.17 *Solar eclipse*

When the Earth passes across the full moon and casts a shadow the Moon appears red and faint. This is called a **lunar eclipse**.

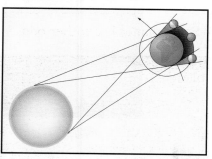

12.18 *Diagram of a lunar eclipse*

12.19 *Lunar eclipse*

In 1998 an Earth spacecraft, *Prospecter*, discovered patches of ice in some deep craters at the poles of the Moon. If the patches of ice were able to melt, a lake 10 km across and 10 m deep would be created.

22 Where does moonlight come from and why is it different at different times?

Find out more about eclipses at ▶ **www.scienceweb.co.uk**

Mars

227.9 million km from the Sun and a red planet comes into view. Mars spins on its axis at an angle of 25°. Its day is 24 hours and 37 minutes. A year on Mars is 687 Earth days. Orbiting around Mars are two moons called Phobos and Deimos.

12.20 *Mars*

Mars has a thin atmosphere of carbon dioxide which means it does not retain heat. This means the temperature is at on average –23°C. It has a polar ice cap of frozen water and solid carbon dioxide. It is thought that Mars was a wet planet in the past.

Mars is only half the size of Earth with a diameter of 6786 km. It is less dense and only one-tenth the mass of Earth.

Mars has an enormous volcano which is three times the height of Everest and so wide it would cover Spain. Luckily it has been extinct for 100 million years. In 1976 two *Viking* spacecraft visited Mars, took photos and analysed the soil. Mars has a low gravity which may be why its atmosphere has not been retained.

Beneath the surface is a dark canyon so deep the Alps could fit inside and leave room to spare. Time to move on into space.

The asteroid belt

This is a dangerous place, like a rubble yard in space with huge lumps of rock milling around. Asteroids were once thought to be the remains of a huge planet but now are thought to be material that never formed a planet. Ceres is the biggest asteroid at 950 km across and was discovered in 1801 by the Italian Giuseppe Piazzi.

Jupiter

778.3 million km from the Sun and ahead is a huge ball of liquid spinning on its axis at an angle of 3°. It spins very fast and a day is only 9 hours 55 minutes but a year is 11.9 Earth years. The fast spinning gives the planet a bulge around its equator.

Orbiting Jupiter are 16 moons. The most exciting of these is Europa. The spacecraft, *Galileo,* revealed what appears to be a frozen ball of ice with fine cracks and an ocean of liquid water underneath.

12.21 *Jupiter*

---

23 Why will it take so long to reach Mars from Earth?

24 Why could Mars be another planet where life could be found?

25 Why would the loss of atmosphere make it difficult for visiting astronauts?

The largest planet circling the Sun, Jupiter is 1300 times bigger than Earth with a diameter of 142,980 km. Yet despite its enormous size it is only 318 times the mass of Earth and a quarter of the density.

Jupiter is made from hydrogen, helium, ammonia and hydrogen cyanide. The average temperature of the planet is –150°C. The most striking feature is the Great Red Spot which is thought to be a permanent great storm like a hurricane. This is not a place where life could exist so I will carry on across the solar system.

Saturn

1427 million km from the Sun and it is very cold out here. There are only a few of us light photons around and so it is quite dark too. Saturn is spectacular with its many ice rings stretching many kilometres into space but so thin they are only 1 km thick. Saturn spins on its axis at an angle of 27° and a day takes 10 hours 39 minutes. Saturn takes 29.5 Earth years to make one revolution of the Sun. Orbiting Saturn are 18 moons.

Saturn is 95 times the mass of Earth but only one-eighth its density. It is nine times the size of Earth at 120,540 km diameter. It is a planet made of gas. The surface temperature is –180°C, cold enough to liquefy some gases.

A spacecraft, *Voyager 1*, visited Saturn in 1980. The probe could not see beneath the clouds of Saturn but it recorded huge hurricane winds. Every 30 years a giant storm erupts on the planet. Winds of 1800 km/h blow around the equator.

12.22 *Saturn*

Uranus

2871 million km from the Sun and tipped at a crazy angle of 83° is Uranus. Around the planet there are 11 narrow rings. This planet has a day of 17 hours 14 minutes and takes 84 years to make one orbit of the Sun. Orbiting Uranus are 17 moons.

Not many light photons make it this far so Uranus is not the brightest of planets. I am not sure I will stay here long. This planet is four times bigger than Earth with a diameter of 51,120 km. It is 15 times heavier than Earth but about the same density

The surface temperature here is –210°C. The surface is made mostly of water surrounded by an atmosphere of hydrogen, helium and methane gases. The *Voyager 2* space probe, which visited in 1986, showed a dull picture of a blue-green globe turning in space.

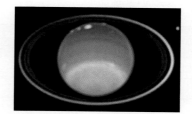

12.23 *Uranus*

Neptune

Into the twilight at 4497 million km from the Sun. It is freezing out here, so cold that the planet is blue with streaks of cloud. There is even the hint of faint rings. This is the world of Neptune, a planet that spins on its axis at 28° and where a day is 16 hours 7 minutes and a year is 165 Earth years. Nearly four times the size of Earth with a diameter of 49,530 km, it is 17 times the mass of the Earth but only 1.6 times as dense.

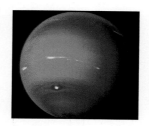

12.24 *Neptune*

The surface temperature of Neptune is –220°C, which is why the methane gas is solid. The weather on Neptune varies from a weak to a strong hurricane with winds 10 times as strong as the fiercest hurricane on Earth. When *Voyager 2* flew past in 1989, it showed a planet with frozen water, white clouds and large dark storms. The probe photographed the surface of Neptune showing a large spot which resembled the Great Red Spot of Jupiter, but years later Neptune's dark spot has disappeared. *Voyager 2* also found six more moons orbiting Neptune making a total of eight moons.

Leaving Neptune I pass Triton – the largest moon. Triton is thought to have originally been a planet caught in the orbit of Neptune which then became a moon. Triton spins in the opposite direction to Neptune. It also has volcanoes which blow huge plumes of gas and debris into the atmosphere. These plumes are caught by the strong winds and blown for long distances.

27 What do the planets Jupiter, Saturn, Uranus and Neptune have in common?

28 What was strange about the way Neptune was discovered?

Pluto

Out here 5914 million km from the Sun it is dark and so cold. Pluto is an icy world. It spins at an angle of 65° and a day is 6 Earth days and 9 Earth hours. A year on Pluto is 248 Earth years.

12.25 *Pluto*

This planet is half the size of Mercury and about one-fifth the size of Earth. It has a diameter of 1170 km and has a mass 0.002 of the Earth. Its density is two-fifths that of the Earth.

Orbiting Pluto is a single moon called Charon. Pluto and Charon always keep the same faces to each other so the moon can only be seen from one side of the planet.

29 Complete the following table and describe any patterns you see in the data.

Planet	Distance from the sun	Diameter of planet	Length of day	Length of year	Number of moons	Main gases in the atmosphere
Mercury						None
Venus						Carbon dioxide
Earth						Nitrogen, oxygen
Mars						Carbon dioxide
Jupiter						Hydrogen, helium
Saturn						Hydrogen, helium
Uranus						Hydrogen, helium, methane
Neptune						Hydrogen, helium, methane
Pluto						Methane

The tenth planet – ice dwarfs

For years astronomers have suspected the existence of a tenth planet. In this search they have found many asteroids in the same region as Pluto. These asteroids are mostly made of frozen water and gases. They are called ice dwarfs and inhabit the Edgeworth–Kuiper Belt, named after the astronomers who found this region. Some of these asteroids have an orbit that brings them so close to the Sun that they begin to melt and become comets.

Questions

1 The following diagram is of the Earth orbiting the Sun.

a The diagram shows one complete Earth orbit of the Sun. How long does this take?

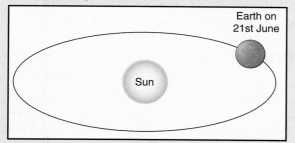

Earth on 21st June

Sun

b Show where the Earth will be on 21st December.

c The 21st June is the day before the summer solstice. What is the summer solstice?

d The 21st December is the day before the winter solstice. What is the winter solstice?

e How different would your shadow be on the two different solstice days? Explain your answer.

f What is an equinox?

2 Label the following diagram of the Earth in orbit.

a 1 is ....

b 2 is ....

c 3 is ....

d 4 is ....

e 5 is ....

f 6 is ....

g 7 is ....

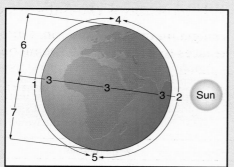

3 Draw the phases of the Moon and explain why there are phases. Explain why there is a period when there is no Moon in the night sky.

4 Throughout the Earth we have time zones.

a Why are there time zones on the Earth?

b Where does time start at zero?

c What is the International Date Line?

d If it is 12 noon in London will be it be light or dark in Hong Kong?

5 The diagram below shows the first six planets in the solar system. The duration of each planet's year is listed in the following table.

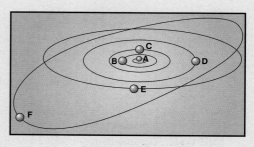

Planet	Distance from the Sun (millions of km)	Year (Earth days)
A	57.9	88
B	108.2	225
C	149.6	365
D	227.9	687
E	778.3	4343
F	1427	10767

a Name the first six planets of the solar system.

b The orbit of planet F is different from that of the other five. Explain what is different.

c Draw a rough graph of distance from the Sun against planet year.

d What conclusions can you draw from the shape of the graph?

6 Complete the following sentences.

a The path a planet follows around the sun is called its ....

b The Moon is a .... of the Earth.

c The Sun is a .... and the Earth is a ....

7 Complete the following paragraph.
The solar system consists of .... spinning or .... the Sun. The inner planets are made from .... while the outer planets are mostly .... The biggest planets are the .... ones.

8 Explain how the Sun produces light. What happens to the light as it moves across the solar system?

9 Explain what a comet is and how comets travel across the solar system.

10 What is the asteroid belt and how do scientists think it was formed?

Glossary

Cells

Asexual reproduction   When an individual organism divides to make two new individuals. The new offspring are genetically identical to the parent.

Cell   The small 'boxes' that all plant and animal tissues are made from.

Cell membrane   The living boundary of an animal cell that allows chemicals in and out of the cell.

Cell wall   The non-living outside layer of a plant cell that supports and strengthens the plant tissues.

Chlorophyll   The green pigment in plant cells, used in photosynthesis to make food.

Chloroplasts   The small bodies in plant cells containing the enzymes needed for photosynthesis.

Cloning   Making a copy of a plant or animal that is identical to the parent.

Cytoplasm   The jelly-like substance in a cell supporting the nucleus.

Division   The process of a cell dividing into two during growth or reproduction.

Gene   The smallest piece of genetic information.

Granule   A small grain. Plant cells may contain granules of starch stored as food. Animal cells may contain granules of keratin making them tough and impermeable, such as in skin.

Magnification   Making an image look bigger so the detail is easier to see.

Nucleus   The part of a cell that contains genetic information.

Organ   A collection of tissues that work together to perform a particular task.

Organisms   The name given to all living things.

Reproduction   The process of making new individuals of any plant or animal species.

System   A set of connected organs that perform a specific task.

Tissue   A collection of cells that all do exactly the same thing.

Vacuole   A space in the centre of a cell filled with fluids needed by the cell.

Variation   The slight difference between different members of the same species.

The environment and feeding relationships

Adaptation   The process of gradual change of a species to suit an environment.

Adapted   Changed to become well suited to a particular environment.

Biosphere   The areas of Earth's surface and atmosphere where living things are found.

Carnivores   Animals that feed on other animals.

Community   All the organisms that share the same habitat.

Decomposers   Living things, such as bacteria and fungi, that feed on dead plants or animals, returning their nutrients to the soil.

Dormant   Alive but not moving or growing.

Ecosystem   The interactions between all living organisms and their environment.

Environment   The surroundings and conditions plants and animals live in.

Food chain   A diagram showing what eats what, consisting of producers and primary and secondary consumers.

Food pyramid   A diagram showing the numbers of different types of animals in an environment.

Food web   A diagram showing how different food chains link together.

Habitat   The natural home of a plant or animal. A habitat must provide all the things the plant or animal needs to survive.

Herbivores   Animals that feed on plants.

Hibernate   To go into a deep seasonal sleep to survive winter conditions. The hibernating animal becomes dormant. Its temperature, breathing rate and heart rate all fall.

Migrate   To move to another area where living conditions are appropriate. Migration is seasonal and normally en masse. Swallows move to Africa for the winter and to Europe for the summer.

Omnivores   Animals that feed on plants and animals.

Predator   An animal that kills other animals for food.

Prey   The animal or type of animal that a predator kills.

Primary consumer   The first consumer in a food chain that eats the producer.

Producers   The plants at the bottom of a food chain that make food from sunlight, carbon dioxide and water.

Quadrat   A small marked-out area to study, for example to search for insect species.

Secondary consumer   A consumer that eats other consumers in a food chain.

Transect   A straight line across an area of study to give a cross section of what plants, animals, habitat types and so on exist in the area.

Reproduction

Embryo The developing young inside an egg or the uterus.

Fallopian tubes The tubes that carry the ova (eggs) from the ovaries to the uterus.

Fertilisation In animals: when the male sperm and female egg join together. In plants: when the male cells in the pollen tube join with the female ovum.

Gametes The special sex cells that join together at fertilisation to make a new individual.

Germination When the seed takes in water and begins to grow roots and shoots using food reserves stored in the seed.

Gestation The time from fertilisation to birth when the embryo grows in the uterus.

Inherited To have a particular characteristic passed on from parent to offspring.

Mature A plant or animal that is in the adult stage of its life cycle.

Menstruation The bleeding that occurs when the blood-rich lining of the uterus is shed at the end of the menstrual cycle. In humans this happens every 28 days.

Nucleus The part of the cell that contains genetic information and controls the growth and activity of the cell.

Ovary One of the female reproductive organs where ova (eggs) are produced.

Ovulation When a fully developed (ripe) egg is released from the ovary. In humans this happens every 28 days from alternate ovaries.

Placenta Tissue which develops in the uterus during pregnancy and is rich in blood capillaries. It transfers nutrients and oxygen from the mother's blood to the developing embryo.

Pollination The transfer of pollen from the male anther to the female stigma of the same species of flower.

Pregnant A female is pregnant when her uterus contains a developing embryo.

Puberty The change from immaturity (childhood) to adulthood when the sexual organs become active and secondary sexual characteristics (body hair, breasts, deeper voice) develop.

Seed The seed develops in flowering plants after fertilisation. It contains all the genetic information needed to grow a new plant, together with a food supply and a hard protective outer case.

Sexual reproduction The type of reproduction that needs both a male and a female plant or animal of the same species or genus.

Sperm The male sex cell in both plants or animals.

Testicles The male reproductive organs where the sperm develop.

Uterus The muscular organ in mammals where the embryo develops before birth.

Variation and classification

Binomial system The modern system of naming and classifying organisms. Each species has a unique name consisting of 2 words: a generic name and a specific name, e.g. *Panthera leo* (lion) and *Panthera tigris* (tiger).

Chordates Animals with a backbone (see **Vertebrates**).

Classification Dividing animals and plants into groups with similar characteristics.

Continuous variation Height in humans is an example of continuous variation. People can be any height and do not belong to natural sets.

Correlation When two things depend on each other so that when one changes the other changes in proportion.

Discontinuous variation Blood group in humans is an example of discontinuous variation. Humans can have blood group A, B, AB or O.

Environment The surroundings and conditions plants and animals live in.

Genus A group of several species of animal or plant with similar characteristics.

Inherited To have a particular characteristic passed on from parent to offspring.

Invertebrates Animals which do not have a backbone (a spine).

Kingdom Living things are divided into animals (the animal kingdom) and plants (the plant kingdom).

Negative correlation Two things are negatively correlated if one increases as the other decreases.

Positive correlation Two things are positively correlated if one increases as the other increases.

Species A group of individuals that share the same set of characteristics (but may show some minor differences) and can breed with each other to produce fertile offspring.

Variation The slight changes that exist between individuals of the same species.

Vertebrates Animals with a backbone (a spine). (See **Chordates**).

The particle theory of matter

Atom The smallest portion of any chemical element.

Compress To squeeze something so it takes up a smaller space.

Compressible Able to be squeezed to take up a smaller space.

Diffusion The spreading out of one substance through another. Diffusion of solids is slower than diffusion of liquids because the molecules move more slowly.

Evidence Facts gathered and used to support an idea or statement.

Expand To spread out to take up a larger volume.

Fluidised bed A bed of granular material such as sand, with gases blown through it to make the particles move about.

Force Simple forces such as pushing and pulling make things move or change. Forces like gravity and electrical or magnetic forces are invisible but their effects can still be seen.

Implode To collapse violently inwards.

Lava The molten rock, often containing gas bubbles, that flows from volcanoes.

Magma The semi-molten layer of rock just below the Earth's crust.

Matter A physical substance which occupies space and possesses mass.

Model A way of representing something to make theories or situations easier to understand.

Particle model The particle model says that all substances are made up of tiny particles that are too small to see.

Pressure The force exerted on each unit area of an object.

Pressurised Raised to a higher pressure than the surroundings or kept at a higher pressure than the surroundings.

Properties The set of characteristics or features that describe something. The properties of solids are: definite shape and volume, high density and slow movement of their particles.

State All matter exists in one of three states – solid, liquid or gas.

Theory An idea or set of ideas explaining something. Before scientists accept a theory as true it has to be supported by evidence from experiments or observations.

Vibrate To move continually to and fro. Atoms vibrate about a central position.

Volcanic eruption When a volcano spurts out gas and molten rock. In a violent volcanic eruption gas and lava can be shot many metres into the air.

Solutions

Alcohol Any of a group of liquids containing an oxygen and hydrogen atom pair (OH). Alcohols are colourless, inflammable and evaporate easily.

Chromatography Separating two or more soluble solids by putting them on absorbent paper and letting very small amounts of water flow through them.

Condensation The process by which a gas turns into liquid when it is cooled or compressed.

Condenser Equipment for condensing gas back into a liquid.

Conserve To keep or protect something, or to keep the quantity of something, such as energy, unchanged.

Dissolve When the molecules of a solid, mix thoroughly with the molecules of water or another liquid so the solid can no longer be seen.

Distillation The process of boiling a liquid and then allowing it to condense again. Distillation produces a pure liquid.

Evaporate When a liquid changes to a gas without being heated to its boiling point.

Evaporation When a liquid changes to a gas without being heated to its boiling point.

Filtering Removing an undissolved solid from a liquid by passing a solution through a membrane which allows the liquid but not the solid particles to pass through.

Insoluble A solid that will not dissolve.

Locating agent A chemical that is added to a reaction to make another, colourless chemical show up.

Mixture Two or more substances that are not chemically joined together, such as iron filings and sand.

Particle model This model says that all material is made up of very tiny particles called atoms. What the atoms do affects what the material is like.

Saturated A solution that contains as much of a dissolved solid as is chemically possible.

Solubility This is a measure of how much of a solid can be dissolved in a certain amount of liquid.

Soluble A solid is soluble if it can be dissolved in a liquid.

Solute The solid that is being dissolved. In brine (salt solution) the solute is salt.

Solution The resulting liquid after a solute (solid) has dissolved in a solvent (liquid).

Solvent The liquid in which a solid is dissolved. In brine the solvent is water.

Acids and alkalis

Acid A substance that will turn litmus paper red. It has a pH value of less than 7.

Acidic Having the qualities of an acid.

Alkali A substance that will turn litmus paper blue. It has a pH value of more than 7.

Alkaline Having the qualities of an alkali.

Caustic Any substance that burns or corrodes organic tissue, such as skin.

Corrosive Any substance that destroys or wears away other substances. Moist air corrodes iron and makes it go rusty.

Hydrochloric acid A common mineral acid.

Indicator Any substance that changes to different colours in acids and alkalis. Litmus paper and universal indicator paper are two common indicators.

Litmus An indicator paper used to tell whether a liquid is acid or alkali.

Mineral acid The mineral acids are hydrochloric, sulphuric and nitric acid.

Neutral Any substance that is neither acid nor alkali. It has a pH value of 7.

Neutralisation Changing the pH of a substance so that it is neutral, with a pH value of 7.

Neutralise Adding acid or alkali to a substance to bring the pH value to 7.

Nitric acid A clear colourless mineral acid made from ammonia.

pH meter Used to measure how acidic or alkaline something is.

pH scale This goes from 1 (very strong acid) to 14 (very strong alkali). 7 is neutral (neither acid nor alkali).

Solution The resulting liquid after a solute (solid) has dissolved in a solvent (liquid).

Sulphuric acid A common mineral acid.

Universal indicator A type of indicator that changes colour from red (very strong acid) to green (neutral) to blue/purple (strong alkali).

Simple chemical reactions

Acid A substance that will turn litmus paper red. It has a pH value of less than 7.

Carbon dioxide A small part (0.03%) of air is carbon dioxide. It is commonly used in fizzy drinks and fire extinguishers.

Carbonates A range of chemicals containing carbon and oxygen atoms.

Chemical reaction When chemicals react with each other to make new chemicals. This happens because their atoms are rearranged into new patterns.

Combustion Burning. Combustion can only happen if there is a supply of oxygen.

Flammable Able to burn.

Fossil fuel Fuels formed from the remains of plants and animals that lived millions of years ago. Coal and oil are fossil fuels.

Fuel Substances that can be burned as a source of energy. The food we eat is sometimes described as our fuel.

Hydrochloric acid A common mineral acid.

Hydrogen The lightest element. It is an explosive gas. Most of the Sun is made of hydrogen. Three-quarters of the mass of the universe is hydrogen.

Irreversible changes These are changes that result in new products. The chemicals cannot be changed back to their original state.

Methane The chemical name for natural gas. It is a fuel. Methane is made from carbon and hydrogen atoms.

Oxide A type of chemical which is produced when something reacts with oxygen, e.g. magnesium oxide, sulphur dioxide.

Oxygen Oxygen makes up 21% of air. Small amounts of oxygen dissolve in water, supporting plant and animal life. Oxygen is needed for combustion.

Particles The fundamental components of all matter and forces.

Phlogiston An imaginary substance that was once thought to exist in all materials that could burn.

Products The new substances created by chemical reactions.

React To change and make another substance change in a chemical reaction.

Reactants Substances that react with each other in a chemical reaction.

Reactivity A measure of the degree that chemicals react with each other.

Reversible changes Changes that can be changed back again. Changes of state due to heating or cooling are reversible changes.

Salt Common salt is sodium chloride. Other salts are made by the reaction of acids with metals.

Sulphuric acid A common mineral acid.

Word equation An equation, using words, to describe the changes that happen in a chemical reaction.

Energy resources

Acid rain Rain water that is slightly acidic because of the chemicals dissolved in it.

Biomass The total quantity of weight of all the living organisms in an area.

Carbohydrate Substances made from carbon, hydrogen and oxygen. Carbohydrates include starches and sugars and provide energy for both plants and animals.

Coal A fossil fuel.

Crude oil A fossil fuel. Crude oil is refined and used in lots of different products, such as petrol, diesel, lubricating oils, paints, plastics, fertilisers and drugs.

Diesel A fuel used in cars, lorries and industrial machinery. It is made from crude oil.

Energy Energy enables people and machinery to do things. There are lots of different types of energy such as kinetic energy, heat, light, chemical energy and electrical energy.

Fossil fuel Fuels formed from the remains of plants or animals that lived millions of years ago. Coal and oil are fossil fuels.

Fossilised Turned into a fossil, a representation in rock of what the living organism was like.

Fuel Substances that can be burned as a source of energy. The food we eat is sometimes described as our fuel.

Fuel cell A cell producing an electric current from a chemical reaction.

Geothermal Thermal (heat) energy that comes from within the Earth.

Global warming The gradual increase in the Earth's temperature caused by man's activities, especially the burning of some fuels.

Greenhouse effect The effect caused by carbon dioxide and sulphur dioxide in the Earth's atmosphere. Heat from the Earth is trapped inside the atmosphere, making the Earth hotter.

Hydroelectric power Electricity that is generated using the energy from moving water.

Joules (J) The units which are used to measure energy. One thousand Joules make a kiloJoule (kJ).

Natural gas Gas that was formed millions of years ago from the remains of dead plants and animals. It is found above coal and oil deposits.

Non-renewable resources Fuel or energy sources that cannot be replaced once they have been used.

Oil Fuel made from crude oil and used in vehicles and industry.

Photosynthesis The process by which plants make food from carbon dioxide, water and sunlight.

Pollution Substances that cause harm to the environment.

Renewable resources Energy sources that can be replaced, such as sunlight, water power, wood and wind power.

Respiration Respiration happens in every living cell and is the process that the cell uses to obtain energy.

Solar Solar energy is energy that comes from the Sun.

Solar cell A cell that uses light energy from the Sun to generate electricity.

Tidal barrage A barrier across a tidal estuary that uses the energy in moving water to generate electricity.

Wind farm An area that generates electricity using lots of turbines turned by wind power.

Electrical circuits

Ammeter   A meter that measures the electric current in a circuit.

Amps   The units used to measure an electric current.

Battery   A series of cells providing the energy in an electrical circuit.

Bulb   A device for changing electrical energy into light energy.

Cell   A device where energy is stored as chemical energy and released into a circuit as electrical energy.

Circuit   A series of electrical devices all connected together so that an electric current flows through them all.

Conductor   A material which allows an electric current to flow through it. Metals are good conductors of electricity. Carbon is also a good conductor.

Current   A flow of electrically charged particles around a circuit that transfer electrical energy from the battery to the devices where it is needed.

Defibrillator   A machine for supplying a carefully controlled electric current to the human heart to restart it when it has stopped beating.

Dimmers   Special resistors used to control the current to bulbs to make them brighter or dimmer.

Electrons   Very small particles which carry an electric charge. They are parts of an atom. When an electric current flows though a wire, electrons are moving.

Fuse   A safety device in a circuit that melts and breaks the flow of electric current if the current gets too large.

Impulse   An electrical signal sent from the brain to the muscles along the nerves.

Insulator   A material which does not allow an electric current to flow through it. Plastics and rubber are good insulators. Electric cable is covered with an insulator for safety.

Nervous system   The system of nerves that carry messages from the sense organs to the brain and from the brain to the muscles.

Neurone   The type of cell that nerves are made from.

Pacemaker   A device giving small electrical signals to the heart to keep it beating rhythmically.

Parallel circuit   A circuit where the current splits into two or more pathways to reach all the components.

Series circuit   A circuit where the current flows on a single pathway through all of the components in turn.

Variable resistor   A resistor that can become easier or harder for the current to flow through, to make the current bigger or smaller.

Voltmeter   A meter that measures the strength of electric current through the component.

Volts   The units that voltage is measured in.

Forces

Air resistance   The force that slows down an object moving through air; it is caused by the air the object displaces as it moves.

Balanced forces   Forces where the force in any direction is exactly cancelled out by an equal force moving in the opposite direction.

Density   A measure of how much matter occupies a given volume. Dense materials have a lot of matter in a given volume so they are heavy.

Drag   The force that acts to slow down a moving object.

Friction   A force that acts between two surfaces sliding over each other, to slow down movement. The rougher the surfaces the more friction there is between them.

Gravity   The attractive force that acts between masses. On Earth a force of gravity pulls all objects towards the centre of the Earth.

Lift   The upward force that acts on objects of a certain shape, such as aeroplane wings, when they move through air.

Lubricant   A liquid or powder placed between moving surfaces to reduce friction.

Mass   A measure of the amount of matter contained in an object. On Earth a mass of 100 g weighs approximately 1 N.

Resistance   The resistance of a material describes how easy it is for a current to flow through it. The greater the resistance of a material, the more difficult it is for electricity to flow through it.

Speed   A measure of how fast something is moving. Speed can be calculated by dividing distance travelled by the time taken.

Unbalanced forces   When the force in any given direction is not exactly cancelled out by an equal force in the opposite direction.

Upthrust   The force that acts upwards on an object moving downwards through a liquid. It is caused by the liquid the object has to displace as it moves.

Volume   A measure of how much space an object takes up.

Weight   The downward force acting on an object due to the force of gravity pulling on its mass.

Solar System

Asteroid   A small rocky object orbiting the Sun.

Atmosphere   The layer of gases that surrounds Earth and some other planets.

Axis   The imaginary line that the Earth (or other planet) can be thought of as spinning on. The axis of the Earth goes from the North Pole to the South Pole.

Comet   Bodies of dust and ice that orbit the Sun in long elliptical orbits. When they are closer to the Sun they warm up to give a long streaming tail of gas.

Day   The length of time it takes for the Earth, or any other planet, to complete one revolution (complete turn) on its own axis.

Eclipse   The temporary blocking of light from the Sun or Moon. Solar eclipses happen when the Moon moves between the Sun and the Earth.

Galaxy   A collection of millions of stars makes up a galaxy. The Sun is one of millions of stars in a galaxy called the Milky Way.

Hemisphere   Half of a sphere. On Earth, the northern hemisphere is the part of the Earth between the Equator and the North Pole.

Inclination   The angle that the Earth's magnetic field makes with the horizontal at a point on the Earth's surface.

Jupiter   The fifth planet out from the Sun. It has 318 times the mass of the Earth and is surrounded by 16 moons.

Luminous   A luminous object is one that gives out light energy, rather than just reflecting light energy that falls on it.

Mars   The fourth planet out from the Sun. It has about one-tenth the mass of Earth and looks reddish in colour.

Mercury   The planet closest to the Sun. It has about one-twentieth the mass of Earth and is only visible just before sunrise and just after sunset.

Moon   The only natural satellite of Earth. It has about one-hundredth the mass of Earth and orbits Earth once every 27.3 days.

Neptune   The eighth planet out from the Sun. It is about four times the radius of the Earth with about 17 times its mass.

Orbit   The path of the planets around the Sun or of a satellite around its planet.

Pluto   The ninth planet out from the Sun and currently the most distant planet known. It is tiny, with a mass of less 0.5% of the mass of Earth.

Probe   An unmanned exploratory spacecraft sent to find out about distant parts of the solar system.

Satellite   A small body that orbits a larger one. The Moon is a satellite of Earth. Earth also has many artificial satellites used for communications and collecting information.

Saturn   The sixth planet out from the Sun. It is the second largest planet with almost one hundred times the mass of the Earth.

Season   Regular variations in temperature and weather caused by the Earth's orbit around the Sun.

Solar System   The Sun together with all the planets and other bodies orbiting around it.

Star   A body in space that radiates light, heat and other forms of electromagnetic radiation.

Telescope   An instrument for examining objects too far away to be seen with the naked eye. Astronomers use telescopes to study distant stars and galaxies.

Time zone   Earth has 24 time zones running north–south. Moving east, the time in each time zone moves on 1 hour, so that the Sun appears overhead at noon everywhere.

Uranus   The seventh planet out from the Sun. It has 14 times the mass of Earth and is surrounded by 17 moons.

Venus   The second planet out from the Sun. It is the closest planet to Earth and is similar in size.

Year   The time it takes a planet to orbit the Sun once. An Earth year is 365.26 days.

Index